Good Ground

~ Volume 1 ~

Good Ground

∽ Volume 1 ∽

Beth Madison

Bennington, Vermont

Good Ground
Volume 1
Copyright © 2022 by Beth Madison

Published by Northeastern Baptist Press
            Post Office Box 4600
            Bennington, VT 05201

Scripture quotations are taken from various translations and indicated at each reference.

Cover design by Leason Stiles

Softcover ISBN: 978-1-953331-17-5

Jude v. 24-25. GNT

Now to him who is able to keep you from stumbling and to present you blameless before the presence of his glory with great joy, to the only God, our Savior, through Jesus Christ our Lord, be glory, majesty, dominion, and authority, before all time and now and forever.

Amen.

Soli Deo Gloria.

CONTENTS

ACKNOWLEDGEMENTS

Dear Jesus,

Thank you for the gift of learning more of You through studying Your creation and Your Word. Thank you for the many people You put in my life so that some of what You've taught me could be shared in these books. Your grace, glory, and goodness are beyond words or imagining. Oh, Jesus, I love You.

Dear friends,

Thank you, each and every one of you. Your encouragement, patience, and prayers are as precious to me as you are. Please know that if you don't see your name here, it's only because of limited page space, not wanting to leave anyone out, and inability to begin to express my gratitude for you in words. Each of you has a special place in my heart for always. I love you.

A very heartfelt thanks for: husband, Andy and parents, Dr. and Mrs. David L. Coffey; colleagues, Drs. Ben Mitchell, Hal and Mary Anne Poe, and Ann Singleton; Union University with special appreciation to the Writing Center; agent, Dr. Sharon Norris Elliott with AuthorizeMe

Literary Agency; and publisher, Northeastern Baptist Press with Drs. Mark Ballard and Tim Christian and Mr. Jacob Thompson.

All mistakes, inadequacies, and should-have-said betters (or not-at-all) are credited only to the author.

1

A GOOD SHOVEL

I have better understanding and deeper insight than all my teachers [because of Your word], for Your testimonies are my meditation.

Psalm 119:99, AMP

A good shovel. Yup, you read it correctly – a good shovel. Realistically, a good shovel is probably not even on the radar of most people as an essential tool for daily life, unless you're a farmer or gardener. Yet a good shovel is the most important tool of a soil scientist. Shovels give soil scientists access to discover more of the amazing world under our feet.

1

Similarly, a Bible is the most important tool of a Christ-follower. I have multiple copies of Scripture scattered throughout my home and try to use my current favorite Bible daily. Yet do I really cherish this copy of God's Word as essential for my day? Do I view it as the tool most used by God to work up the soil of my soul as to farm it for a rich harvest of His kingdom work to nourish others? Do I treasure it as a chosen tool in the hands of the Master to cultivate the true life of Christ in the garden of my heart?

The soil under our feet provides and sustains life for plants, microbes, animals, and people in a myriad of ways. Similarly, the soil of our souls can be life-giving conduits for people living in our homes, communities, and world in a myriad of ways. And my hope for all of us with these *Good Ground* books is that we learn more of the much more that is our God, the Creator and Sustainer of the soil under our feet and in our souls.

For soil scientists, soil is the final frontier in its wondrously beautiful, diverse, and complex relationships that impact our world in ways beyond our comprehension, and even our imaginations...for example, did you know that two of the three antibiotics in typical over-the-counter antibiotic creams were first isolated from soil? Or that modern sewage treatment system designs are based on how soil acts as a natural water filter? Or that more microbes can live in one cubic centimeter of healthy soil than people living on our entire planet? And that's just a peep through the keyhole into the vast world under our feet.

Shovels crack the door to this amazing world of soil often overlooked or unknown outside of the occasional road-cut, drainage ditch, or construction site. The freshly sharpened edge of a square-bladed Arkansas sharpshooter shovel can slice neatly through thick grasses, tree roots, and hardened soil crusts to bring up a clean whole piece of creation, if wielded properly. Afterwards, a sharp unbent posthole digger-shaped auger shovel can then bring up sample after sample of a world chock-full of life in a progression deeper and deeper down into the ground. Each individual piece of soil can tell a soil scientist more of the story of the soil's past, present, and (potential) future, if she knows how to read its pages.

Learning how to read a soil's book requires lots of humility, patience, determination, hard work, and time. This truth applies to the soil under our feet and in our souls. Just as each soil's unique properties come from the influence and combination of five major soil-forming factors (climate, time, parent material, topography, biota), the language of a soil is expressed in its physical, chemical, and biological properties. Similarly, the language of our souls is expressed in our choices, responses, and beliefs. Both the soil under our feet and in our souls has been crafted with purpose and potential, dependent on how we choose to utilize and care for them now and in the future.

For a soil scientist to learn about even one of the over 20,000 different soil types in the United States alone, she must dig lots of holes, both in the soil and in her preconceived ideas about what she thinks a soil is or should be. But some truths are constant, independent of soil type or location. Soils are unique just like people. Soils are valuable just like people. Soils respond differently just like people. Many times, the true value of a soil has to be unearthed with a good shovel, because at first glance, the soil might just be considered dirt, similar to how we might tend to think about people we don't know (see 1 Samuel 16:7).

Broadly speaking, dirt is simply soil out-of-place needing to be washed out of clothes, mopped from floors, or scraped off of shoes. Dirt is soil which is now inconvenient or unwanted rather than the essential natural resource it was when in its place of service. A favorite saying by soil scientists is "we've got to stop treating our soil like dirt" in regards to the need for the increased awareness of preventing soil erosion and its associated problems. Soil is considered a renewable resource when speaking like a geologist in spans of time such as eras or epochs covering thousands of years, in contrast to the real-world time we live in today. For example, it takes about two thousand years for six inches of soil to form from bedrock in contrast with the potential for an overnight loss of that same six inches of soil from a mismanaged field deluged by rainstorms. From soil to dirt in less than twelve hours is more common than most soil scientists like to think. And it takes far more than a good shovel to try and move the once-soil, now-dirt back into place in hopes of trying to recover the now-lost pieces of creation that had potential for feeding, healing, or cleaning our world. And for this soil scientist, the same principle applies to the soil of my soul lost to past sins' ravages on my life from regret, guilt, and shame that try to erode away the particles of my fragile faith.

Good shovels wielded by trained soil scientists can accomplish a lot but no one can reform or replace soil except the One Who created it and made man from it (see Genesis 2:7). Just as "God don't make no junk" with people, God don't make no dirt with soil. He made soils and souls and gave purpose to all. And there in His purpose and plan, we can find satisfaction for our souls as we meet with Him in study of Scripture and of soil science with the worldview of He alone is the One Who made and holds all things together (see Colossians 1:15-17).

As Christians, we are called to be caretakers of both soils and souls, whether or not we are soil scientists or theologians. We are ambassadors of the Holy One Who spoke creation into being and sustains it still from the ground up. There is no soul or soil outside of His presence or our prayers. Our prayers can yield the good work of the Holy Spirit, wielding the good sharp shovel of Scripture deep into the soil of that soul running as hard as she can from the One Who created her…this soil scientist is living proof of that truth…

For only the power of God is strong enough, sharp enough, to break through the crusted-over heart of a soul eroded away by sin and left as a fragile, empty, and barren ground devoid of joy, hope, or faith. Only His power can bring up sample after sample of needed repentance for confession and forgiveness in preparation for restoration and renewal. For when that deep and hidden sinful ground is broken up and divided joint from marrow by Scripture's shovel (see Hebrews 4:12), then Creator God can and will reform and replace it with the good soil of a soul rich in humility, obedience, patience, trust, quietness, and perseverance.

The fact that our Creator God is gracious and kind in his relentless cultivation of our hearts and lives is why this soil scientist (temporarily) traded her shovel for a pen to share some of the blessings found in the gift of good ground. The good ground under our feet can remind us of the need for good ground in our souls. The necessary components of good ground, of steadfastness, humility, obedience, vision, exultation, and love, are not easily developed but always bear a rich harvest for those who receive them (see Hebrews 6:7).

Since soil scientists love acronyms as much as theologians, here's one that captures this principle of those six essential components of good ground (steadfastness, humility, obedience, vision, exaltation, love). S.H.O.V.E.L. Six. Habits. Of. Victoriously. Expectant. Living. This kind of life isn't reserved for soil scientists or theologians but is open to anyone desiring good soil to be formed in his or her soul. So, if you're ready to start seeing good ground develop in the gardens of your life, start expecting change in the soil of your soul from the Holy Spirit at work with the shovel of Scripture. He will do the good work of making our lives good ground for His kingdom, if we choose to trust Him with the soil of our souls, starting now.

❧

To help maximize good ground development in your life today, please be sure and complete the digging deeper section at the end of every chapter in both *Good Ground* books, specifically in *Volume 1* now and *Volume 2* which is coming soon. Remember that humility, patience, determination, hard work, and time are required to learn to read a soil and to renew a soul.

Digging Deeper

Take some time to look up, write out, and meditate on each of the Scriptures presented in this chapter.

1. Genesis 2:7   2. 1 Samuel 16:7

3. Colossians 1:15–17   4. Hebrews 4:12

5. Hebrews 6:7   6. Matthew 13:23

Good Ground

What Scripture(s) made you stop and think about the status of the soil of your heart today? And why? (Note: you are not limited to those verses listed in this chapter, be especially conscious of those other verses brought to your mind and heart by the Holy Spirit).

What Scripture(s) do you need to return to tomorrow to receive more of the Holy Spirit's work on the soil of your heart? Why?

Which of the six essential components of good ground do you think you need the most for your soul today? Steadfastness, humility, obedience, vision, exaltation, or love, and why?

If you are able, collect some soil and put it in a clear glass jar (with a lid). (The soil can come from your yard, garden, near-by park, potted plants, or wherever you can find a handful to bring home with you. Potting soil will also work for this.) Plan on keeping this jar near and in clear view while you're doing this study. Take another jar (clear or not, but with a lid) to put with the soil jar. The purpose of this second jar is to hold small index cards or paper scraps upon which you've written Scripture verses that speak deeply to you during this study. These verses will be nourishment for the soil of your soul, for now and for the future. My hope and prayer for you in this study is that when you see soil, you will see Scripture and thus, then continue in *grow[ing] in the grace and knowledge of our Lord and Savior Jesus Christ. To him be the glory both now and to the day of eternity. Amen* (2 Peter 3:18, ESV).

Take some time to pray for the continued good work of God to be done in the soil of your soul and life today. Write down at least three things you are thankful for today.

Reflection prayer:

> *Dear Father,*
>
> *Thank you for your beautiful creation all around me and your sustained care of everything You have made. Thank you that You are always providing beauty for me to discover and to remind me of You and Your tender mercies made new every morning. Thank You that You are the One Who stays and keeps my soul even closer than the soil under my feet. Please help me to long for the quiet I can only find in Your Presence through obedience. Please help me to love You and those around me in better, deeper ways.*
>
> *In the strong Name of Jesus,*
>
> *Amen.*

2

WHAT'S IN A NAME?

"I'll make each conqueror a pillar in the sanctuary of my God, a permanent position of honor. Then I'll write names on you, the pillars: the Name of my God, the Name of God's City—the new Jerusalem coming down out of Heaven—and my new Name."
Revelation 3:12, MSG

My husband and I are called by nicknames from our middle names. Needless to say, this can make for some confusing, if not frustrating, moments when legal documents are involved to prove that this is indeed the real me. However, the upside to this is that I immediately know if it's a salesperson on the phone if they ask for me by my first name. For if they knew me personally, they would be asking for me by my nickname.

I come from a family that loves nicknames, both as regular everyday names (Beth for Elisabeth) and as cherished expressions of love (baby, sweetheart). Nicknames also have a life of their own with me, in that I have been known to refer to those drivers making poor choices on the road as "darling" or "dear". Likewise, I am guilty of side-eye rolls and a clamped jaw towards those who call me "honey" while dismissing me as ignorant and unworthy of making a valid contribution to a conversation. (Yes, I'm working on my arrogant attitude in such situations but I've still a LONG way to go towards grace and humility!)

Having said all that, I think it's fascinating that the same names can have multiple different meanings to different people. The differences in meaning arise from differences in relationship, location, time, understanding, emotions, and other such variables. These differences don't have to be large in proportion for their impact to be large in application. This principle is especially true in soil science where a soil's name is literally comprised of pieces of words indicating the soil's nature, location, age, association with other soils, and such.

A trained soil scientist can read a soil's scientific name and immediately have a picture in her head of its position in the landscape, climate, what parent material it formed from, age, soil texture, drainage and productivity, native vegetation, and on and on…even without a photograph of the soil in the sidebar on the page. All of this information gained from the name itself! In contrast, someone who is not a soil scientist can read the same name and gain nothing. The time spent looking at the name garners no new knowledge of the soil because she doesn't know the relationship between the name and its meaning.

For example, if I refer to a fine, mixed, mesic Typic Paleudalf, *trained* soil scientists will get the picture in their heads of a well-drained, fertile, very deep and dark-colored soil, having horizons with primarily silty soil textures, overlying a phosphatic limestone parent material usually found on an upland level topography in a moderately humid climate. Such a picture can then help facilitate good decision-making on best management practices for this soil type – be it row-crop farming, building a road or structure(s), forestry, and the like, for sustainability of this valuable natural soil resource for now and for the future.

Similarly, if I'm referring to a Maury silt loam, a soil scientist familiar with this soil type will get the same picture in her head as if I'd said a fine, mixed, mesic Typic Paleudalf because the Maury silt loam is a particular subset of this soil type. In my opinion, the term Maury silt loam is almost like a nickname for the fine, mixed, mesic Typic Paleudalf soils.

In the scientific nomenclature for soils, each piece of the soil's scientific name refers to a specific characteristic of that soil. The name, Paleudalf, breaks down into pieces indicating the weathered (pale-) Alfisol soil order (-alf) found in a humid climate (-ud-). However, the common name (or nickname), Maury silt loam, of the same soil often indicates the county where it was first formally classified (Maury) or the person who first classified it along with its primary soil texture (silt loam). This common name nomenclature is similar to common names for birds, plants, microbes, and other organisms as to give recognition to its discovery by location or by person.

Remember how I emphasized earlier that *trained* soil scientists would immediately recognize the characteristics of a particular soil by reading or hearing its specific scientific name? Not all soil scientists automatically know the nomenclature system well enough to be able to delineate between specific climates and topographical locations and the like – only those soil scientists with extended training in soil taxonomy, which is itself a specialized subset of study within soil science. To other soil scientists, such as soil microbiologists, soil chemists, and soil physicists, including those experts outstanding in their fields (pun intended!), these names could be unfamiliar. Unfamiliar in the sense they would be asking for someone on the phone by her first name because they didn't know the person went by her nickname…

The choice to call someone by a particular name (Beth or Dr. Madison, sweetheart or ma'am, neighbor or professor) often indicates the closeness and strength of the relationship and thus, the knowledge and experience one has of and with that person. Such choices in nomenclature are not reserved for soils or people but also extends to God in the name(s) which I choose to call Him because of the way I know Him (e.g., Father and Lord) and/or the way I need for Him to show Himself to me now (e.g., *the strength of my heart and my portion forever*, Psalm 73:26, ESV). God chose specific nomenclature to show Himself in Scripture to specific people at specific times. His choice of name, *I Am,* indicated important truths He wanted to impress upon the people with whom He was speaking. He told Abraham that He was his shield; Moses that He was the God of his fathers; Joshua that He was with him; and onwards through the Old Testament. Similarly, Hagar, David, and others also chose specific nomenclature to recognize God and address certain features of His character through such names as *El Roi, the God who sees me* (Genesis 16:13). These names were rich in meaning to both parties in the relationship as they indicated trust for: expectations of promises to be kept and fulfilled; deliverance in seemingly impossible circumstances; and provision for now and the unknown future. The names themselves were pictures in the minds of the people pointing them to the Christ who was to come – the Messiah, Jesus our Savior.

Yet the Israelite people didn't recognize Jesus as their Messiah because the picture in their heads wasn't that of a baby born in a stable to a young mother and a carpenter. Even the expectations of the disciples didn't include a humble servant who washed feet, dined with tax collectors, or talked with lepers and sinful women. And when confronted with the truth of *whoever has seen Me has seen the Father* (John 14:9b, ESV), these same disciples were still unbelieving because the picture in front of them of *Emmanuel, God with us,* didn't line up with their chosen names for Him of *Rabbi* or *Lord*, reflecting their lack of a deeper, intimate knowledge and relationship with Him as the One True God. I wonder if the words Jesus spoke to the disciples in John 14 went over their heads like reading a list of scientific soil names to a group of toddlers? The disciples were untrained to recognize the truth of Christ before the Resurrection and thus, couldn't recognize Jesus to be the same God Who introduced Himself as the *I Am* to their forefathers.

And today, with a myriad of readily available Bible study resources at my fingertips, I often think that I am as untrained as the disciples at recognizing Jesus at work in my everyday world. I have one ear listening for the trumpet call of Christ's return with the other ear ignoring the cries of those neighbors, students, and family members who need agape love poured into their lives in tangible ways. My eyes scan the heavens for glimpses of the glory to come while being blind to the injustice, apathy, and discontent rampant in my world and in my own heart. My lips sing words rich in hope of God's power while my mind is running numbers and scenarios to try and figure out how to purchase yet another thing that will rust, decay, and fade away.

As C.S. Lewis would say, I am "far too easily satisfied" with my containable, frame-able picture of Jesus rather than trying to know and understand who He truly is – *the One Who was, Who is, and Who is to come, the Almighty* (Revelation 4:8, ESV) and the One who is *the image of the invisible God...in whom all things hold togeth-*

er (Colossians 1:15-17, ESV). The same One Who spoke creation into being with its tens of thousands of different types of soils, animals, plants, microorganisms, and people is this same Jesus Who sees me here, now, just like He did with Abraham, Moses, Joshua, Hagar, David, and all who called out His Name in years past.

My mind's picture is far too small, weak, poor, and limited to begin to display the fullness of the Name of Christ because my relationship is far too small, weak, poor, and limited to begin to understand the fullness of Him. Even though I may call out His Name in prayer, my own constrained expectations of His power to be at work in my life and others' lives keeps me from taking a death-grip on the mustard seed faith that moves mountains.

Yet Jesus doesn't reject me in my lack of knowledge and faith. He doesn't tell me to go and get more training and then try again. He tells me to come to Him and learn from Him and in so doing, to find rest, strength, peace, joy, and hope in Him, the One who is above all names (see Matthew 11:28-30). And when I come, He doesn't call out my sins by name; He puts an end to them. He doesn't just say my name; He calls me beloved, chosen, called, righteous daughter. He tells me that my name is engraved on the palms of His hands (see Isaiah 49:16) and written in His book of eternal life (see Revelation 3:5), for now and forever. These truths far exceed even what I dare try and picture in my mind as gloriously good!

If that wasn't enough, He tells me that one day He will mark me with His Name so that everyone can clearly see that I am His – *"I'll make each conqueror a pillar in the sanctuary of my God, a permanent position of honor. Then I'll write names on you, the pillars: the Name of my God, the Name of God's City—the new Jerusalem coming down out of Heaven—and my new Name"* (Revelation 3:12, MSG).

And for this soil scientist mired in the clay of the now and not yet, the very thought of that day is beyond what words can name, much less define…

Digging Deeper

Take some time to look up, write out, and meditate on each of the Scriptures presented in this chapter.

1. Revelation 3:12   2. Psalm 73:26   3. Genesis 16:13

4. John 14:9   5. Revelation 4:8   6. Colossians 1:15-17

7. Matthew 11:28-30   8. Revelation 3:5

What Scripture(s) made you stop and think about the status of the soil of your heart today? And why? (Note: you are not limited to those verses listed in this chapter, be especially conscious of those other verses brought to your mind and heart by the Holy Spirit).

What's in a Name?

What Scripture(s) do you need to return to tomorrow to receive more of the Holy Spirit's work on the soil of your heart? Why?

Write down your full name and your nickname(s) if you have them. Which of these names do you prefer and why? What is your favorite name for God? Why did you choose this name for Him? What memories do you have that are linked with this name for God?

Write down the names (or initials or meaningful letters to represent) of 2-3 people in your life who don't know God well enough to call Him by Name. Now sign and date next to this list as a commitment to pray for these people. If possible, consider putting their names/initials/letters into your calendar as a reminder to pray for them and to invest your life into theirs through conversations (especially listening) and activities that will show them love like Jesus would.

Which of the six essential components of good ground do you think you need the most today for your soul? Humility, obedience, patience, trust, quietness, or perseverance. Why?

Good Ground

Take some time to pray for the continued good work of God to be done in the soil of your soul and life today. Write down at least three things you are thankful for today.

Reflection prayer:

Dear Father,

Thank You that Your Name is holy and above all names. Thank You that Your Name brings peace, hope, courage, and joy to all situations. Thank You that Your Name is for forever and for today. Please help me to cherish You by calling out Your Name in praise and in need. Please help me to love others by praying for them in Your Name and telling them about You.

In the strong Name of Jesus,

Amen.

3

NOTHING IS WASTED

Not only that, but we rejoice in our sufferings, knowing that
suffering produces endurance, and endurance produces character,
and character produces hope, and hope does not put us to shame,
because God's love has been poured into our hearts through the
Holy Spirit who has been given to us.
Romans 5:3–5, ESV

Have you ever been treasure hunting? (Trust me, this is way different than snipe hunting!) If so, what treasure were you looking for? Did you find it? All of us probably have very different ideas as to what we consider treasure. Yet all of us probably know treasure when we find it, *if* we are able to find it…

Good Ground

Take a minute now to stop and write down three things you would consider as treasure that you are searching for in your life today. Then write down three different things that you already have that you consider as treasures. You may write these in the margin or on another sheet of paper – just make sure and hold on to them until we get to the end of this chapter.

When I was growing up, my father and I often went "treasure hunting" or at least that's how I remember our walks through the woods, farm, neighborhood, and even the backyard on occasion. We never came home without our pockets full of "treasure"—interesting rocks, leaves, sticks, flowers, bugs, and the stray nut, bolt, screw, hat, mitten, sock, or such. To this day, when we walk either together or by ourselves, we still come home with something jangling, clinking, or disintegrating in our pockets.

Many would consider our treasures to be trash—castoffs, mismatched, rusty, broken, decaying pieces of what should've been left where we saw it. But we see beauty and usefulness in each piece—that splash of color, that unusual shape or texture, that piece to replace what I lost last month on another of my adventures or will need for next week's project or repair.

In soil science, we live by the principle that "one man's trash is another man's treasure" in embracing the hidden beauty of agricultural waste application as a valuable soil amendment for farmland. Both liquid and solid agricultural waste are chock-full of the treasures of organic matter, nutrients, and water which are all essential additives for a healthy soil. That manure, compost, sewage, or wastewater is treasure in the eyes of a soil scientist because you are getting nutrients, water, organic matter, and microorganisms in one perfect package. (Granted, I don't want to put any of that in my pockets, but I would like a truckload or two for my yard and garden. These scraped subdivision soils need all the help they can get!)

"Black gold," "free money," and other such terms are lovingly used by farmers to describe the true worth of solid and liquid agricultural waste to current and future productivity when they're applied to soil. In fact, my father just today emailed me a picture of his spinach crop happily growing in a new application of incorporated manure in his backyard garden. This manure is and will be providing a readily available source of plant nutrients and water to his crops throughout the season. Afterwards, his soil will be bettered for future crops because of the increased total soil organic matter content, promotion of soil micro- and macro-organism populations and improved drainage, chemical activity, pH, and nearly everything else you want to happen to promote soil health. Even one application of waste to soil can produce measurable effects on current and future soil health and thus, on current and future productivity of that soil for crop yield.

Yet the public perception of using agricultural waste as a valuable soil amendment is often that of fear and disgust because of lack of knowledge. As a soil scientist, I'm frequently asked, "What is the best thing I can do for my yard, garden, or flower bed?." My response of "manure or compost" is often received with disbelief, disgust, or denial unless this person has used or known someone who has used manure or compost in their yard or garden. And if they had, then the response is (usually), "Yes! I have never had such big and pretty grass, tomatoes, or roses!" along with, "Do you know where I can get some more for this year?".

An important soil science fact about waste application in agriculture: for the waste itself to have reached the status of "now that's good stuff!" it must undergo a series of decay reactions. These reactions are carried out by microbes to bring the nutrient percentages in the waste into proper ratios that promote crop growth, rather than hinder it. In other words, if the amount of carbon in the waste is much higher than the nitrogen amounts (called the C:N ratio), the waste isn't a good soil additive for an actively growing crop. This is because if the C:N ratio of the waste is higher than the natural C:N ratio of the soil, the microbes in the soil and in the waste can take away essential nitrogen from the crop, instead of being a source of nitrogen to the crop (which is usually the reason waste is added to the soil). Needless to say, sufficient time for allowing these decay reactions to decrease the C:N ratios is required so that the waste addition will be helpful to the growing crop.

A good round value for a desired C:N ratio in waste for soil application to a garden or yard is less than 20:1. Practically, most places don't advertise their C:N ratios of the waste you can obtain, but a rule of thumb is that if the waste looks (and smells) "old", it might be in or at least close to the desired ratio. If it's obviously fresh, letting it "sit in the corner" for a while is always a good choice before application. For if you don't give the waste enough time to decay, both in physical size and in nutrient ratios, the waste will truly be waste for the crop because of the potential loss in desired crop productivity at harvest.

So while thinking about all of this a few days ago, I made a connection to Romans 5:3-5 (ESV): *Not only that, but we rejoice in our sufferings, knowing that suffering produces endurance, and endurance produces character, and character produces hope, and hope does not put us to shame, because God's love has been poured into our hearts through the Holy Spirit who has been given to us.* The connection that I'm seeing as a Christian and a soil scientist is that many times what I perceive as unwanted additions (waste) to my life (trials, challenges, suffering, persecution) are the very things which bring about much-needed changes in my heart, both for now and for the future. That which I wouldn't choose for myself (much less want to put in my pockets to take home) because I consider them trials are the very treasures which display the beauty of grace and love by nourishing the growth of the fruit of the Spirit (see Galatians 5:22-23) in my life in ways that nothing else can. These sufferings cause a decay of my pride which leads to growth of humility as they are changing me into one who endures and hopes. These sufferings have potential to change the very character of the soil of my soul and life more into the likeness of Christ by the workings of the Holy Spirit alive in me. For when my ratio of self to Christ has been properly decreased, then I am ready to be useful soil to promote the beauty of His love, grace, hope, and joy to a world dying around me without eternal life in Christ. And frequently, much time is required for the suffering to produce the needed decrease of me and increase of Christ in my life…I don't like waiting any more than anyone, but I have learned that seemingly "sitting in the corner" time of waiting is actually when the Holy Spirit is at work doing the good work of changing the soil of my soul. And the soil of my soul demands a me to Christ ratio of 0:100 all of the time – anything less just isn't healthy for any part of me or those in the gardens of my life.

The series of decay reactions in my pride and in me are essential for real growth to occur. This kind of growth in character is not measured by piled-up achievements, but in those thoughts, choices, and emotions (such as patience, forgiveness, and understanding) which I choose to cherish as honoring Christ. Stepping back instead of pushing forward, staying quiet instead of speaking up, and such indicate I have grown in obedience and trust, and thus, faith. These choices are hard-won tangible evidence of the growing health and vigor of the soil of my soul and life because I have found the true value and treasure in what I used to consider waste (see Matthew 26:6-13).

Just like farmers who used to reject conservation tillage farming methods because they were afraid they would be considered lazy or inept for having dirty fields covered with residue, Christians who are undergoing suffering (and its effect of a life that often looks messy in pain, grief, and loss) are often afraid of being considered to be lacking in faith. Others who haven't learned the true value of suffering as a valuable amendment to one's life for bringing glory to God and good to his people (see John chapter 9) can judge those in suffering to be lazy, inept, and poor in faith. Before suffering entered my life, I was one of those Christians who judged messy lives as simply being undisciplined, lazy, or inept. I used to think this because I was deceived that "if I believe hard enough, all will be good" or worse yet, the deception that "I can do all things by myself and for myself." This lie permeates our culture of "I got this," where suffering is often seen as the inability to overcome that which is undesirable and thus, a life wasted.

Yet I've found this inability to overcome is precious treasure ripe with freedom and hope because there is vibrant joy in surrender and obedience (see Psalm 119:32 and 45). That which I desperately tried to remove from my life as unwanted (chronic illness) has turned out to be the very amendment which has brought true life in this season and in whatever seasons God has for my life to come. Those who don't recognize the value of suffering ask me, "How can you have joy in this?" They don't understand that what they think is waste is indeed treasure to me because it has brought me closer to Christ. (And the hope that I've found in Christ overflows even the deepest of pockets!) Honestly, this trial of chronic illness still makes getting through most days as hard as shoveling chicken manure, but I wouldn't trade it for anything because of what God has taught me in it—He truly is my treasure for today and forever (see Isaiah 33:6).

Digging Deeper

Re-read your treasure lists from the beginning of this chapter. Do you have anything to add or subtract from those lists? If so, make the changes now.

Take some time to look up, write out, and meditate on each of the Scriptures presented in this chapter.

1. Romans 5:3-5   2. Galatians 5:22-23

3. Matthew 26:6-13   4. John 9:1-9

5. Psalm 119:32, 45   6. Isaiah 33:6

What Scripture(s) made you stop and think about the status of the soil of your heart today and why? (Note: you are not limited to those verses listed in this chapter, be especially conscious of those other verses brought to your mind and heart by the Holy Spirit).

What Scripture(s) do you need to return to tomorrow to receive more of the Holy Spirit's work on the soil of your heart? Why?

Which of the six essential components of good ground do you think you need the most today for your soul? Humility, obedience, patience, trust, quietness, or perseverance. And why?

Take some time to pray for the continued good work of God to be done in the soil of your soul and life today. Write down at least three things you are thankful for today.

Pull out your treasure lists one more time. Are any of the things you're thankful for today on your treasure lists? If so, why? If not, why not?

Here's one more chance to make changes to your treasure lists in view of what you've learned from the Scriptures in this chapter... do your treasure lists reflect your worldview of Christ as Creator, Provider, and Sustainer of all things, including your life today?

Good Ground

Reflection prayer:

Dear Father,

Thank You that You don't just make things and set them aside. Thank You that You keep remaking and revealing new things, even and especially in those things that I take for granted. Please open my eyes today to see the true treasure in what You've placed in my life. And please help change my heart to treasure You above all else – there is none like You, Lord! Please help my life show others that You alone are worth pursuing above all else.

In the strong Name of Jesus,

Amen.

4

BURIED TREASURES

Your word have I treasured in my heart
that I might not sin against You.
Psalm 119:11, NASB

Like I talked about in the previous chapter, treasure hunting can be a wonderful adventure. What's the best treasure you've ever found? Worms, bugs, rocks, old plant roots, broken pieces of who-knows-what, and other such treasures that could fit in our pockets, to the chagrin of our mothers, are completely valid answers here....

If you can't remember your most memorable treasure or treasure hunt, have you had the treasure of watching children digging for buried treasure? If not, see if you can borrow a friend's child (or two) for a digging for treasure adventure in an old field or backyard or abandoned garden where you've gone the day before and hidden such treasures as coins, small toys, or shiny rocks for these children to joyously discover and for you to delight in their abundant enthusiasm. And while you're delighting in their joy, let God etch this picture on your mind of how He delights in you discovering more of the treasures of His creation and the ultimate Treasure of Him.

Take a minute now to stop and read Zephaniah 3:17.

Even as a little child, I enjoyed the feel of soil on my fingers and better yet – the mix of soil and water to make mud pies for my stuffed animals and dolls (who didn't always return home in the same condition in which they left for these adventures, much to the chagrin of my mother). And then, when I was older, I had the task of making potting soil from its components in the greenhouse - pouring the peat moss, vermiculite, and finely ground bark into an old horse trough and almost climbing in myself to be able to mix it thoroughly with my hands, arms, and shoulders because I was so small. This task was then followed by another favorite job: filling small pots with this potting soil; lining them up in trays; and poking little holes in the soil for the seeds of whatever plants we were starting at the time. Now a favorite task is taking students into the field or woods and digging holes with a soil auger to see how the soil changes vertically in a profile and horizontally over the landscape. Best of all, now I can go and dig holes to my heart's delight;

call it teaching or research; and not worry about getting in trouble for coming home covered in mud! (like yesterday, from which my pants are still soaking in the hopes I can get them clean just one more time).

To many soil scientists, one of the greatest buried treasures in soil is that of the vast amounts of carbon trapped in deep plant roots or recalcitrant (very resistant to decomposition) organic matter. Such deep roots and organic matter materials are often compressed, dense, and lignified ("woody") and thus, quite resistant to decay by soil microorganisms. Therefore, the carbon in these materials is considered as "set aside" or sequestered from the global atmospheric carbon cycle just like a sequestered jury is set aside and kept apart from every outside influence during a court trial. This sequestered carbon is considered removed from this cycle, because of the extremely slow decomposition rates of upwards of hundreds of years. Thus, this sequestered carbon is very important in its influence on current and potentially future global atmospheric carbon dioxide levels.

Sequestered carbon may seem unimportant at first glance, but the implications of sequestered carbon on the global carbon cycle can be vast in its impact on (hopefully) slowing the process of global warming. Because the more carbon that is sequestered in soil, the less there is in the atmosphere in the form of carbon dioxide. Carbon dioxide concentrations are major players in global warming through their influence on trapping more and more amounts of heat from sunlight radiation.

All too often, the terms global warming and greenhouse effect are mistakenly used interchangeably. These terms do not mean the same thing. Global warming is the increase in our planet's mean global temperatures over time, independent of the reason for this increase. The greenhouse effect is the trapping of heat near the earth's surface by the atmosphere allowing sunlight to pass through it but not allowing the heat generated from the sunlight to pass back out of the atmosphere. The earth's greenhouse effect is essential for life on our planet to exist. Without it, temperatures would be too hot during the day and too cold at night. Think about a greenhouse in the winter where the glass lets the sunlight pass through for plant growth while also trapping enough heat for the plants to thrive in the cold temperatures.

But think for a minute, what happens to the plants in the greenhouse when spring or summer comes? The glass is still letting in the sunlight and trapping the heat but now the temperatures are too high for the plants to thrive. Then the windows and doors to the greenhouse are opened for venting, the release of the trapped warm air and drawing in of cooler outside air to bring the greenhouse environment back in line with what the plants need. This principle is similar to our earth's greenhouse effect and life here on earth. Our earth's atmosphere is thickening with gases like carbon dioxide, methane, and nitrous oxides, and is trapping too much heat for us to thrive…Yet we don't have the option of opening windows in our earth's atmosphere to release the too-warm air and return us to an overall cooler mean global temperature more suited for our lives as people, plants, animals, and microbes.

We don't have opportunity to thin our atmosphere of current levels of greenhouse gases but we do have opportunity to slow their rates of increasing concentrations. We can do this by reducing fossil fuel use, increasing fuel use efficiency, and other conservation measures including increasing sequestered carbon amounts in soils. Greater amounts of sequestered carbon in soils have the potential to slow the rate of ever-increasing global atmospheric carbon dioxide concentrations which in turn, can influence the subsequent rise of mean global temperatures, i.e. global warming.

Yet the amazing world under our feet is often overlooked as a major player in global warming with its important role as a reservoir for sequestered carbon that used to be in the atmosphere as carbon dioxide. Soil is the second largest sink (long-term holding area) for carbon dioxide on our planet, after oceans. However, our first largest sink, oceans, has an annual turn-over of deep water containing high carbon dioxide levels coming to the surface where some of the trapped carbon dioxide is released from the water. In contrast, sequestered carbon in soils can remain indefinitely trapped if the soil is not plowed, drained, or otherwise exposed to oxygen.

Sequestered carbon-containing materials in soils are usually in a low oxygen environment deep in the soil or in a wetland soils environment where aerobic bacteria (aerobes require oxygen) are absent or in a resting state. These environments usually are dominated by anaerobic bacteria not requiring oxygen because they use elements other than oxygen for life and growth. Anaerobic bacteria are much less efficient in energy conversion, growth, and thus, decay of organic matter containing sequestered carbon. Therefore, the carbon dioxide trapped there is much more likely to stay there as sequestered carbon because the anaerobic bacteria won't be quickly breaking down the carbon-containing materials.

Another easily overlooked fact about soil as a carbon sink is that the below-ground portion of a healthy actively growing plant is at least as big (if not up to twice as big) as the above-ground portion. Now that's a lot of biomass (living carbon-containing material)! And if this below-ground biomass portion (roots) grows deep and becomes lignified, these roots can hold a lot of carbon dioxide that was taken from the atmosphere by the above-ground portion of the plant during photosynthesis. Plus, if the plant is healthy with good vigorous growth, it will be taking carbon from the atmosphere through photosynthesis at a faster rate than it is returning carbon to the atmosphere through respiration. This means even more carbon dioxide can be deposited into the roots for long-term storage as sequestered carbon. Usually the bigger the tree, the deeper and woodier the root system, thus, the greater the potential for more sequestered carbon.

While we're talking about photosynthesis, let's stop and ponder this for a moment – carbon dioxide, the chemical we are discarding as waste from our vehicles, factories, fireplaces, and mouths is the exact same chemical that plants require for photosynthesis, the reaction that ultimately supplies our world with energy trapped from sunlight. Talk about GRACE! God designed photosynthesis to be the most wonderful recycling program on earth working in tandem with the most essential and important energy conversion reaction on earth. And that's not all, photosynthesis also gives us oxygen which is another most precious commodity! The numerous interactions occurring in the many steps of photosynthesis become even more intricate, beautiful, and amazing the deeper you dive into the myriad of details in the processes, compounds, and participating organisms themselves, but that's ripe fodder for yet another book...

Even as intimately acquainted as I am with plants, soils, and the processes occurring in the world under my feet, I often overlook or worse yet, take for granted, the many beautiful treasures of our natural world-be they sunlight, plants, soils, oxygen, photosynthesis, nutrient cycling, or carbon sequestration. They are those things that go on day after day without my input or attention. Yet if they were to disappear or change, my world would fundamentally be changed.

Just as fundamentally important to my days as plants, soils, carbon dioxide, and photosynthesis, is the daily need for me to choose to bow my head, heart and mind to seek God through digging deep in Scripture for memorization and study as with Psalm 119:11 (NASB) *Your word have I treasured in my heart that I might not sin against You.* Choosing to seek God in the treasure of Scripture can dramatically change the environment of my heart and the atmosphere of my days, no matter the circumstances in my life at the time.

Many times, buried treasures of Scripture in my heart and mind are the only things holding me and my faith together in hard circumstances which threaten to decay my trust in God. Yet these truths are most important when they are not sequestered from the rest of my life. For when they are allowed to permeate every particle of my life, they will produce change when wielded by the Holy Spirit on my life. For when I am looking at my circumstances only as I see them on the surface, I forget those buried treasures of truth that God is faithful, loving, gracious, kind, merciful, forgiving, and ever-present. Nothing can limit, much less sequester, my Almighty God!

Those dense woody Scriptural truths, if buried and treasured in my heart and mind, will always be present to remind me of God's unchanging, unfailing promises of staying with me, giving strength to me, and going before and behind me. And in turn, these recalcitrant truths help me make the better choices of remaining: quiet as the temperature (and volume) of others around me increases in an atmosphere thick with anger or fear; hopeful when the diagnosis looms as a hard, dark storm in the near distance; standing when all I really want to do is bury my head in the sand; and stable when my world seems to be quickly draining or decomposing all around me. God alone is my deep-down stability. He alone can sequester me and keep me away from all these fears in an undeniable kept-apart quietness of soul. He alone is my treasure forever.

These promises and so many others in Scripture help guard my heart and mind in Christ Jesus against the erosive power of worry (see Philippians 4:7-8). They reorient my choices towards humility and patience, neither of which are naturally occurring in my heart's soil and both of which are easily degraded by a climate of challenging circumstances. God's promises help cultivate the soil of my soul to make it a fertile field for God to use in the lives of others.

Many days and nights especially, I find myself saying aloud those treasures of Scripture which were buried in my heart and mind as a child – Proverbs 3:5-6, *Trust in the Lord with all your heart and lean not unto your own understanding but in all your ways, acknowledge Him, and He will make straight your paths* (ESV); Romans 8:38-39, *For I am sure, that neither death nor life, nor angels nor rulers, nor things present nor things to come, nor powers, nor height nor depth, nor anything else in all creation, will be able to separate us from the love of God in Christ Jesus* (ESV); and Psalm 23 in its entirety, usually whispered with tears dripping and bowed head like I learned from my father whose heart is a most fertile soil for the work of His Savior.

Unearthing these buried truths by saying them aloud to myself and my children as they grew opened new fields for the planting of seeds of faith, hope, and love through further study and discussion. And now, each act of hearing these promises sends even deeper roots of a vigorous faith into my heart's soil to store up a harvest of faith, hope, and love that doesn't degrade even when exposed to the air of the harsh reality of grief and pain from the loss of a child, betrayal by close friends, and chronic disease and disability. These losses and others have cut deep furrows of grief, loss, and pain into my heart and life. But my most gracious God keeps incorporating His strong love to soften and strengthen for making the soil of my soul to be the *adamah ("fertile earth")* necessary for a faithful life. He never stops his good work of growing my faith as long as I keep humbly listening, watching, and waiting for that which is true, lasting, and wise as in Proverbs 8:34, *Blessed is the man who listens to me, watching daily at my gates, waiting at my doorposts* (ESV). Trust me, this isn't an easy or quickly done task, but it is a task with great reward.

Thirty years ago, Andy and I had Bible verses special to us printed on laminated cards as gifts for the guests at our wedding. Hebrews 6:7 was one of my favorite verses then and still is today - *Land that drinks in the rain often falling upon it and that produces a crop useful for whom it is farmed will receive the blessing of God* (NIV). Will you let this soil scientist excavate some of the hidden beauty in this verse? If so, read on...

Only soil that is simultaneously soft and strong can do the work of receiving rain, storing it, and then returning it to the crop as needed for health and growth, especially that of fruit or grain production. Soil like this is referred to as 'friable' by a soil scientist. A friable soil is one that has been carefully crafted by its Creator at its beginning and carefully tended by its caretaker(s) over time. Naturally rich in nutrients, responsive to additives, and workable with proper management techniques, a friable soil is often a very deep and productive soil well-suited for growing a variety of crops.

A friable soil is an *adamah* kind of soil. But even with such a soil, much work, time, and patience are required for a good harvest (see James 5:7). Yet, if you're anything like me, you want the fruit of knowing the promises of Scripture without the work of receiving the truth of them or the work of memorizing them. Work, hard work at that, is required to set in these verses of Scripture so that they are there, fixed, rooted, ready for when I need to counter my doubts during the dry times of trusting, waiting, or listening when life just doesn't go the way I'd planned, much less hoped for. Scripture reframes my thoughts when it seems that my life is sequestered in the waiting and the longing for the now and not yet. Only such truths can expose me and my stubborn, lignified and, deep-rooted arrogance, to the need for the plowing of repentance. And then for the need for constancy in obedience in those times when I struggle with doing what I know is right rather than what I want to do, which is unfortunately every single day.

In college, I first fell in love with using index cards for learning both science and Scripture. Writing the equation, term, or process on one side of the card and the definition or results on the other was the best way for me to receive the scientific information and store it up for when I needed it for an exam. And more importantly, then and now, the same principle works for me with Scripture verses. All through college and graduate school, I would carry both science and Scripture cards around everywhere and pull them out to study whenever I had a spare moment – be it waiting at the doctor's office, at a red light, in line at the grocery, before class started, while experiments or supper were cooking. (Side note: both then and now, my cooking consists of experiments which don't always turn out as expected, much less hoped for, but my wonderful husband always eats them most graciously.)

Today I am still using index cards for memorizing Scripture which seems to take far more work now to become buried treasures in my heart and mind because of stress, pain, responsibilities, and age. But this work of digging deep and burying truth is most definitely worth the doing because I long for that *adamah* kind of soil, of a heart and life that keeps bearing fruit in old age as with Psalm 92:14. Promises like Psalm 92:14 don't decay but grow richer and more valuable with age and can impact me for now and others for generations to come. As I age, truths like Isaiah 46:4, *Even to your old age and gray hairs I am he, I am he who will sustain you. I have made you and I will carry you; I will sustain you and I will rescue you* (NIV), become even more precious as buried treasures in the soil of my heart and life. And I hope that they might do the same for you too…

Digging Deeper

Take some time to look up, write out, and meditate on each of the Scriptures presented in this chapter.

1. Psalm 119:11   2. Zephaniah 3:17

3. Matthew 13:23   4. Philippians 4:7-8

5. Proverbs 3:5-6   6. Romans 8:38-39

7. Psalm 23 (savor this one in the reading of it aloud)

8. Proverbs 8:34   9. Hebrews 6:7   10. James 5:7

11. Psalm 92:14   12. Isaiah 46:4

What Scripture(s) made you stop and think about the status of the soil of your heart today? Why? (Note: you are not limited to those verses listed in this chapter, be especially conscious of those other verses brought to your mind and heart by the Holy Spirit).

What Scripture(s) do you need to return to tomorrow to receive more of the Holy Spirit's work on the soil of your heart and why?

Which of the six essential components of good ground do you think you need the most today for your soul? Humility, obedience, patience, trust, quietness, or perseverance. Why?

Choose at least one of the verses listed above or one that has been brought to your mind during the study of this chapter and write it out on an index card or something similar to start memorizing today. Consider making a habit of Scripture memorization if this is not part of your regular routine. Consider marking your calendar with a certain day each week to repeat this process and another day each week to review verses previously memorized to keep them buried firmly in your heart and mind.

Now, think about at least one person you can share this verse with who might be encouraged or edified through hearing it from you in a phone call or audio message or reading it from you in a text, email, Facebook, Twitter, or Instagram posting. Take the time to send this verse out now or plan to do it no later than by the end of tomorrow.

Write his or her name here as a reminder to share the verse with him or her. Also, be sure and pray for the Holy Spirit to use this verse to change the heart of your friend (and your own heart) into good soil for the Savior.

Take some time to pray for the continued good work of God to be done in the soil of your soul and life today. Write down at least three things you are thankful for today.

Reflection prayer:

Dear Father,

Thank you that You are always putting Scripture in front of me and patiently teaching me to treasure it and You. Thank you that You never give up on cultivating truth in my life and the lives of others in my life. Please help me to choose You over arrogance so that You might make my heart's soil into adamah for Your harvest of souls. Please help me to study and memorize Scripture and then bring them to my mind so I can encourage and exhort others to seek You. Thank You for all of Your promises and that You are true to all of them, all of the time.

In the strong Name of Jesus,

Amen.

5

THE BEST
EXCHANGE EVER

God had Christ, who was sinless, take our sin
so that we might receive God's approval through him.
2 Corinthians 5:21, GW

One of the most confusing, headache-provoking, and abstract concepts in soil science is cation exchange capacity (CEC) I'll be explaining this fully in just a bit – but in case you can't wait, CEC is the exchange of positively charged atoms (cations) held on soil particles with those cations in the water around the soil particles. On that note, thank you in advance for extending even more patience and grace in your reading to this old absent-minded eccentric soil science professor in this chapter. I'm so grateful to be here with you as we learn together about our most gracious Christ Jesus and His creation.

I can still remember thinking when I first learned about CEC in my first soil science course as a sophomore in college, "Just how am I supposed to understand this anyway?". I also had similar thoughts in the many subsequent advanced soil science courses I had as an undergraduate and graduate student. Then the first time I taught this concept as a newly-minted instructor, I can remember thinking, "Now if I can't understand this principle myself, how in the world can I try and teach it to my students?" And now, almost 25 years later, I am still over here grinding my teeth with a churning stomach from the stress of trying to explain this same potentially confusing concept while writing this chapter for you. But thankfully, together we can learn from our Father Who created, understood, and prepared all of creation, including and especially CEC, and us for this moment with Him in this moment of humble worship of Him. So, let's plunge together into the deep end of both soil science and Scriptural thought and wait in expectation for our Good God to teach us. May He use His Word to unearth new thoughts for us to delight in His Presence and return our praise to Him from the soil of our souls. And thank you, dear reader, for holding my hand – it does help me to be brave when we jump into these ideas together as friends!

The Best Exchange Ever

Cation exchange capacity (CEC) is an indispensable life-giving process in a healthy soil. This process gives soil the ability to provide essential nutrients to a growing crop throughout the growing season or life of the plants. CEC is also vital in how it keeps a soil's pH level relatively constant over time. A buffering or maintenance of a constant pH level over time is also essential for nutrient availability and the general health of a crop growing in a soil.

Soil is naturally negatively charged which means it attracts the positively charged plant-essential nutrients and holds onto them, as according to the basic chemical principle of "opposites attract and likes repulse." (I will restrain myself at this time from giving forth on this concept as applied to human relationships. Yes, my students shake their heads in dismay at such awful jokes too...) Even if sufficient amounts of plant nutrients for the entire growing season are applied in fertilizer, these nutrients will not be provided to the crop as it grows during the season without the action of CEC at work in the soil. Because without CEC, these nutrients would either be washed off the soil surface or down through the soil profile and then somewhere else, by rain or irrigation waters. If this washing off occurs, then other potentially worse problems of pollution of surrounding water bodies and natural habitats can result from the nutrients transported in the waters moving through or over the soil.

A soil's CEC primarily comes from the clay and the soil organic matter (SOM) in the soil. The larger sand and silt particles in a soil provide some CEC but to a much lesser extent than the clay or SOM fractions because of their lower surface area to volume ratios and decreased amount of overall net negative charge. The chemistry behind that principle is that the ratio of surface area to volume usually increases as the size of the object decreases. For example, think about the surface area of a baseball in comparison with a basketball as a picture of this surface area to volume ratio.

Since the clay and SOM fractions in soil are huge in negatively charged surfaces, they are ideal environments for thousands of simultaneous chemical reactions. The size scale of clays tops out at 0.002 mm in diameter and goes all the way down to microscopic. Think about those extremely fine-grained white sands that seem like dust in the wind, except when stuck between your toes and your shoes...the very biggest clay particles are at least 100 times smaller than even those seemingly tiny sand particles more un-countable and numerous than Abraham's offspring (see Genesis 32:12).

Plus, clays have vast amounts of internal area because the internal structure of each clay particle is like that of stacked dinner plates. Reactions can occur not just on the outside surfaces of the clays but on all the surfaces in between the "plates." Also, these clay "plates" can expand and contract to absorb or release chemicals in response to chemical concentrations around them, thus exposing even more surface area for even more chemical reactions. Isn't our God simply amazing in how He thought of and then created such structures as these tiny clay particles that do such big and necessary tasks for us without our understanding or input (see Isaiah 55:8-9)?

Chemical concentrations in the soil are the driving force for the chemical reactions occurring during cation exchange between the soil and the plant. Just as materials flow naturally from areas of high concentration to areas of low concentration via diffusion, the chemicals being exchanged in CEC reactions do the same. This flow pattern is almost as if the soil is "pumping" out positively charged plant nutrient ions (cations) from where they are in high concentration on the clay and SOM surfaces to the areas of low nutrient concentration around the actively growing plant roots.

The plant nutrient concentrations in soil are naturally low around the plant roots because the roots are taking in the nutrients from the soil. And in turn, the soil is taking up those chemicals onto the organic and inorganic particles that the plant roots are "pumping" out as waste in order to maintain their proper internal chemical levels. Hence, therein lies the reasoning for the name of cation exchange capacity.

This same principle of exchange also applies to the soil's natural pH buffering capacity which occurs because of CEC. With buffering capacity, the soil particles absorb naturally pH lowering hydrogen ions from the soil solution which were previously given off by the plant roots as waste. In converse, the soil emits naturally occurring buffering cations in exchange for the absorbed hydrogen ions. This exchange of hydrogen for buffering cations helps keep the soil pH closer to neutral. Thus, CEC acts as a natural means of allaying soil acidification in a soil as it weathers (or "ages") over time. Another way to think of soil aging regarding CEC is as the normal and gradual loss of a soil's innate net negative charge from the soil particles and thus, its ability to exchange ions in the soil solution. This loss could be comparable to the expected and gradual loss of strength or vigor with aging in humans.

This pH buffering capacity in soils from CEC helps to keep the plant essential nutrients in forms the plant can absorb and use for growth. An acid pH in soil can cause some plant nutrients to change into forms the plant can't use while also creating an environment favorable for toxic levels of detrimental non-plant nutrient ions in the soil. These issues related to soil pH are especially prevalent in soils in the Southeastern U.S. where soils are usually "older" from faster weathering in a hot, wet climate of more easily degraded parent materials and naturally lower amounts of SOM than in cooler, drier climates. Lime and other soil amendments are frequently added to increase soil pH closer to neutral thereby increasing the concentrations of plant essential nutrients while decreasing concentrations of toxic non-plant nutrients. However, these amendments still cannot replace the contribution of native CEC from clays and SOM to the general health of a soil and its innate plant nutrition supply capacity. And in turn, the general health and plant nutrition supply capacity of the soil ultimately affect crop productivity, independent of the "age" of the soil.

Whew! That was a lot of chemistry, wasn't it! Let's take a deep breath together and get to the spiritual connection that I'm seeing with CEC, Scripture, and the soil of our souls...

Nearly the same time I was first learning about CEC in soils in college, I fell head over heels in love with one of my favorite verses of all time, 2 Corinthians 5:21 (GW) *God had Christ, who was sinless, take our sin so that we might receive God's approval through him.* Today I still don't understand CEC, much less this verse, to their fullest which makes me even more appreciative of this verse as the most glorious exchange ever! And after talking with others far more learned than me, I don't think I'm alone in not being able to understand the glorious exchange Christ made for sinners like me.

The exchange of my sin for Christ's righteousness – literally, my waste for the righteousness of God imparted to me by Christ for today and forever, is as mind-blowing a concept now as it was over thirty years ago. Now that I'm older and know more of my sin and its far-reaching implications in others' lives, this concept is even more amazing. Just as plants can't provide nutrients for themselves because they are dependent on what they receive from the soil via CEC, I can receive righteousness only through God's grace and my faith in the death, burial, and resurrection of the sinless Christ as fully God and fully man (see Ephesians 2:8-9). And Christ didn't do this just for me, He did it for all who would receive him (see John 3:16-17). Only Christ could accomplish what no one else could achieve.

Jesus Christ did this once for all, once forever (see Romans 6:10 and Hebrews 10:10). Yet He gives me the privilege, the joy, and the gift of remembering the waste of my sin in the full assurance that it has been exchanged for salvation *by grace through faith* (Ephesians 2:8, CSB). This is the most magnificent exchange ever! This exchange alone would be far more than I could ever ask or imagine as per Ephesians 3:20, but the exchanges don't stop there...

Creator God provides daily for my needs in a myriad of ways just as He does for all of creation, including the sparrows and lilies (see Matthew 6:28). He gives fullness, abundance, and grace, in all ways, to my life in Him (see Colossians 2:10), even if I don't choose to exchange my arrogance for His grace-gifts. He alone provides those essentials that I might not even realize (or often overlook) are needed for daily life and growth - such things as beauty for ashes, gladness for mourning, praise for weakness (Isaiah 61:3); dancing for mourning, gladness for weeping (Psalm 30:11); compassion and caring for anxious thoughts (1 Peter 5:7); and other such marvelous exchanges. He alone is capable of all these exchanges if I will but come to Him as in Matthew 11:28-30, *Come to me, all who labor and are heavy laden, and I will give you rest. Take my yoke upon you and learn from me, for I am gentle and lowly in heart, and you will find rest for your souls. For my yoke is easy, and my burden is light* (ESV). Again, such a glorious exchange – an unequaled full measure of rest for my striving which has accomplished nothing for me except the depletion of the soil of my soul of the necessary nutrients of hope and joy. Yet He does exchange restoration and renewal for even the smallest mustard seed of faith.

Honestly, the exchanging of my agenda for His plan is often not what I like or choose. Yet when I finally do humble myself and come to Him for this exchange, He always provides that quietness of soul rest that I can't obtain anywhere else. And only this true soul rest gives the *peace that passes all understanding* able to guard my heart and mind from all the chaos trying to take me over (Philippians 4:7). In turn, this peace helps me hear that Jesus daily calls me to the life-giving exchanges of apathy for love, humility for pride, longsuffering for impatience, forgiveness for bitterness, trust for worry, judgment for mercy, truth for lies, rest for striving, and eternity for now. Most times, I don't like these exchanges. Yet I know they are necessary for growth, both for me and for others in my world, especially those who haven't found my magnificent Jesus for themselves yet.

Jesus knows exactly where the people who desperately need Him are at all times. Hence, He plans my days to give me the opportunity and resources necessary to respond to them with the love, humility, longsuffering, and such that He has already given to me. Such responses don't buffer the anger, hurt, or fear lodged in their hearts, but rather show them that grace is resilient and available to them, if they choose to accept it. As importantly, such responses remind me of the incredible grace poured out onto me every single day.

It's hard to respond as Jesus would to those whose choices and words are increasing the acidity in my stomach and unrest in my heart. Yet Jesus reminds me that He dearly loves them (and me) and that I can't create the peace He gives; I can only receive it in exchange for my arrogance. Only Jesus is strong enough to exchange my reactions of anger for responses of obedience and slowly, patiently change the soil of my soul to be more like His. For when my soul becomes more and more like His, it can be that *adamah* ("fertile soil") for His purposes and His people. And only then is my soul's soil ready to pray for and respond lovingly to those who desperately need to know His love and His peace for now and forever in the most glorious exchange of His forgiveness for their sin.

Digging Deeper

Take some time to look up, write out or read (as specified), and meditate on each of the Scriptures presented in this chapter.

1. 2 Corinthians 5:21   2. Genesis 32:12

3. Isaiah 55:8-9   4. Ephesians 2:8-9   5. John 3:16-17

6. Romans 6:10   7. Hebrews 10:10   8. Ephesians 3:21

9. Matthew 6:28   10. Colossians 2:10   11. Isaiah 61:3

12. Psalm 30:11   13. 1 Peter 5:7

14. Matthew 11:28-30   15. Philippians 4:7

What Scripture(s) made you stop and think about the status of the soil of your soul today? Why? (Note: you are not limited to those verses listed in this chapter, be especially conscious of those other verses brought to your mind and heart by the Holy Spirit).

What Scripture(s) do you need to return to tomorrow to receive more of the Holy Spirit's work on the soil of your heart and why?

If you're a to-do list maker like me, you probably love checking off the tasks as you complete them. (Confession: yes, sometimes I add things I've already done to the list just to have the pleasure of checking them off!) If so, get out your list for today (or tomorrow) and look at it in this new way: what on my to-do list needs exchanging for an opportunity to show God's love to someone else? Write down at least 2 items or people that come to mind for this from your list. Think on and pray for God to show you how to exchange your agendas for His purpose and people. After you've completed the items with the people God brought to mind, come back and look at the next day's to-do list. Consider making "showing grace and love to others" as a line-item on your to-do lists and watch for how God in turn, gives you the rest of Matthew 11:28-30 for your agendas.

Similarly, what are your go-to responses for when someone: cuts you off in traffic; blames you for something you didn't do or ignores you for something you did; cuts in line in front of you at the store; uses up the last of the milk/bread/chips/cookies that you were planning on having; interrupts your day with their emergency from lack of planning; dismisses your ideas as stupid or takes your ideas and gets the credit for them as their own; or ignores you or curses you without cause? Is grace your first or second or never response to these or other life situations? Take some time to examine the soil of your soul in your responses to others while praying for God to plant even more seeds of grace in your life starting now.

Which of the six essential components of good ground do you think you need the most today for your soul? Steadfastness, humility, obedience, vision, exaltation, and love. And why?

Take some time to pray for the continued good work of God to be done in the soil of your soul and life today. Write down at least three things you are thankful for today.

Reflection prayer:

> *Dear Father,*
>
> *Thank you for the glorious exchange of Jesus for my sin. Thank You for making a way for me to be restored to You in righteousness. Thank You that I couldn't accomplish it on my own but that You planned for this since before the foundation of the world. Thank You that You keep on working in my life to make me more like Jesus by helping me to exchange my plans for Your purpose and will. Please show me today how You want me to exchange my thoughts, words, and actions for Your grace and love extended to others in my life. Please keep reminding me of the mind-blowing grace You give me and them every single day.*
>
> *In the strong Name of Jesus,*
>
> *Amen.*

6

Repeat, This Is Just a Test

...but test everything; hold fast to what is good.
1 Thessalonians 5:21, ESV

Soil testing has been occurring for many years in many different ways and for many different purposes. The overarching purpose of soil testing is to see if this soil can perform this task, be it the task of crop production, building or road construction, septic tank capability, wildlife habitat, temporary water storage from offsite drainage, etc. There are a variety of tests for the variety of purposes, especially that of crop production.

Soil testing involves a variety of methods, equipment, and outcomes. Tests for soil can range from field tests of testing the soil for pH levels or rubbing it between fingers and thumb for soil texture or soil moisture to laboratory tests of atomic level mass spectrometry for amounts and distribution of specific elements or molecules. Yet the purpose of soil testing remains the same – to see if this soil can do this task in a way that accomplishes the desires of those doing the tests on the soil.

Historically, it took quite a few years to convince many farmers that professional soil testing for soil nutrient levels and pH was worth the time and money. Now, most farmers have a strict regimen of soil testing in their management plans because the tests really do pay for themselves. The cost of testing is far exceeded by profits from increased crop productivity and decreased costs for unnecessary soil additions or treatments. Many lawn care or turf management companies are fully sold on using soil testing, along with the dedicated home gardener who has marked soil testing dates as highlighted reminders on her calendar.

As discussed earlier in the section on cation exchange capacity (CEC), soil is the primary reservoir from which plants obtain their essential nutrients. There are seventeen plant essential nutrients which vary in the amounts and functions necessary for plant growth. These plant essential nutrients are carbon, boron, hydrogen, oxygen, phosphorus, potassium, nitrogen, sulfur, copper, zinc, calcium, iron, magnesium, manganese, chloride, molybdenum, and nickel. I still remember the mnemonic I learned over 30 years ago in my introduction to plant science course for remembering these nutrients – C B HOPKNS CuZn CaFe Mg Mn Cl Mo Ni – "C B Hopkins cousin's café [which is] mighty good, mighty nice [but] closed [on] Monday nights" (why yes, you're welcome for that memory aid!).

Some of these nutrients are required in hundreds of pounds per acre (nitrogen) while others are only required in tiny amounts (molybdenum at less than two ounces per acre). Whether a plant nutrient is a macronutrient (large amounts needed) or a micronutrient (small amounts needed), all of these nutrients are required in their specific amounts at specific times in specific plant-available forms for maximum crop growth and productivity. An abundance of sixteen other plant essential nutrients cannot fully compensate for the deficiency of one nutrient in its potential long-lasting and far-reaching implications on crop productivity. Every nutrient is important.

The availability of many of these plant-essential nutrients for use by a crop is dependent on soil texture, soil pH, and soil moisture content. All of these soil properties are common variables tested for by farmers and gardeners. Just because a nutrient is present in the soil in sufficient amounts for maximum crop productivity doesn't mean that it's in a form the crop can use. There can be a huge difference between the total amount of a plant essential nutrient in a soil and the amount of that nutrient that the plants can use. Soil tests can tell the farmer/gardener the following: how much of the nutrients are present in the soil; if the nutrients are in an available form for the plant to use; and if the soil itself has the potential to make the nutrients available to the crop over the growing season, with or without additional management choices. Soil tests can give insight into both the health of the soil and of the growing crop or crops yet to be planted.

Another reason for soil testing is that many plant nutrient deficiencies can be mimicked, not only by plant diseases, but also by other nutrient deficiencies. For example, sulfur deficiency symptoms in corn (not common) can look the same as nitrogen deficiency (very common) in leaf yellowing or striping and weak, stunted, or thinned-out plant growth. Thus, the first and very logical choice when you see this problem in the field would be to apply more nitrogen fertilizer if you haven't done a soil test. Yet applying more nitrogen is merely wasted money and potential off-site pollution from the excess nitrogen fertilizer if the real culprit is the unavailability of sulfur in the soil. Most soils usually have plenty of naturally occurring sulfur from their parent materials of various types of bedrock, but the sulfur can be in a form in the soil that's not available for plant use, if there's a problem with soil pH. Sulfur deficiency is usually only determined by a soil test for both soil pH and plant available soil sulfur concentrations. Knowledge of both test results is important because many times, the best solution for sulfur deficiency is adding a soil-acidifying amendment such as gypsum, manure, or certain composts.

Collecting a representative soil sample for soil testing is as vital as the proper conduction of the various tests to be done on the soil sample. Every part of a field that's different from any of the other parts (such as topography, past treatments, plant types, drainage, soil texture, etc.) needs to have its own separate soil sample for soil testing purposes. Closely similar parts of a field can be properly tested by combining smaller soil samples into a larger soil sample that has been mixed well before pulling a sample for testing from it. Most farmers will be sending in multiple soil samples for analysis at multiple times during the year.

Thorough representation of differences in the soil of a field is important in many ways. For example, if you have areas of a field not represented in the soil samples collected, the data from the soil tests won't be applicable for these areas. Thus, these areas could be over or under-treated with fertilizer or any other amendment applied for maximizing crop productivity. Over-application of soil amendments (especially fertilizer) can then result in inefficient use of resources which will lower a profit margin even further. In turn, this smaller margin can impact the farmer's plans which are usually on a knife edge of survival or loss in today's economy which threatens to topple even more family farms into simply being fond memories of past generations.

The pennies paid for soil testing can quickly and easily convert to dollars earned at harvest if care is taken in the sampling and testing procedures and subsequent management choices are made according to the test results. The on-site or do-it-yourself at-home kits for soil testing have improved greatly over the years. Yet as a whole, they still do not compare in their overall usefulness with the conventional tests done at large laboratories with specialized equipment, regimented analyses, and trained personnel doing frequent tests for precision and accuracy compared to standards run in the testing cycles.

These principles for proper soil testing for maximizing crop productivity remind me of some principles we are commanded to follow for our lives laid out in Scripture such as 1 Thessalonians 5:21, *but test everything, and hold fast to what is good* (ESV). Being naturally lazy, my first inclination is to want to believe, trust, and obey a principle that makes me feel good, rather than believing, trusting, and obeying a principle that is true, but hard. I like those things that seem easy with fast results, not the much needed something that requires solid, committed, everyday diligent work.

I want everything in my life to be both easily available and helpful to me without the work, time, and resources required for the testing, evaluation, and incorporation of potentially life-changing principles into my life. For example, I want the desires of my heart given to me without the choices required for delighting myself in God (see Psalm 37:4). I want the straight paths in life without the constant trusting, committing, and acknowledging of God alone (see Proverbs 3:5-6). I want the full fruits of a rich harvest now without having to go through the day-after-day hard steps of testing to see if how I am acting, thinking, and living line up with what is true from Scripture (see 1 Thessalonians 5:21).

And worse yet, if the principles I'm holding onto in my life don't line up with Scripture, I admit I often don't want to make the appropriate changes in my life to prevent the further degradation by sin of the soil of my soul and life and subsequent effects of offsite pollution by my sin on others' lives. Plainly said, I want the harvest without the hard work.

Yet I know, both as a Christian and as a farm girl, that harvest doesn't occur without hard work, and lots of it. When I read the following excerpt from the authorized biography of Elisabeth Elliot, this quote reached out and grabbed me by the throat - "For Elisabeth, the central question was not 'How does this make me feel?' but simply, 'Is this true?'. If so, then the next question was 'What do I need to do about it to obey God?' *Boom.*"[1] That quote encapsulates the principle from 1 Thessalonians 5:21 (ICB) – *test everything. Keep what is good.*

Far more than a curated closet, minimalist home, or well-managed farm, garden, or yard, this principle demands that I correctly assess every part of my life – is it true in lining up with what Scripture says is true? If so, then keep it. If not, then work needs to be done for its removal. For this principle is actually a lie acting as a disease or deficiency in my life, preventing the life of Christ from thriving at maximum productivity in the soil of my soul and thus, my life. Many times, testing life-principles like these requires more than at-home kits of self-help books or studies. True deep life-analysis often requires the time, dedication, and costs of open confession and accountability to a trusted fellow Christian who knows what is true, clings to it in his or her life, and speaks to me in love about what isn't true in my life (see Ephesians 4:15). A wise friend like this can better test and see what needed truth is deficient in my life or what disease threatens to overtake and destroy my life. Selfishly, I want to dismiss my deficiencies in humility, selflessness, patience, and perseverance as something I can easily treat with more time spent listening to another sermon or reading another book, all the while ignoring the need for the application of truth in repentance, prayer, and obedience. The problem isn't the problem here. I'm merely improperly treating what I think is one kind of deficiency by adding the wrong nutrient and not fixing the problem. The soil of my soul is still lacking what is really needed. Only the testing of my life's beliefs by the application of Scriptural truth spoken in love with a heaping measure of grace can begin to remediate the soil of this stubborn soil scientist's soul and life. Unfortunately, many times the soil of my soul is too acidic from arrogance and hard from crusted-over unrepentance to receive the much-needed amendments of grace and mercy. But thankfully, my Jesus is persistent in the application of his soul-softening love that changes the pH of the soil of my soul thereby, making other essential nutrients of hope, joy, faith, and courage available to me for strength to keep testing and trusting for the now and for the kingdom to come.

Yet when I do receive the treatment of truth into the soil of my soul, the seeds of my trust in my Jesus grow deeper in the knowledge of such truths that He is the strong tower I can run to and be saved (see Proverbs 18:10); He is the Good Shepherd who cares for me in all ways (see Psalm 23 and John 10); He is faithful to forgive and restore (see 1 John 1:9); and so many other truths that are now available for growth in the hopes of a one-day Matthew 13:23 *30, 60, or 100-fold harvest.*

For when my heart has been changed to line up with the standards of truth set forth in Scripture, then I am ready for more growth as in James 1:2-4, *Count it all joy, my brothers, when you meet trials of various kinds, for you know that the testing of your faith produces steadfastness. And let steadfastness have its full effect, that you may be perfect and complete, lacking in nothing* (ESV). Steadfastness is an essential component for rich, vibrant maturity in Christ – that kind of life that produces the *100-fold harvest.* That unwavering clinging to what is good, while testing everything, is an essential nutrient for Christ-like living in a world that tries to convince me, "all that glitters is gold" in direct opposition to the truth in Job 23:10b, *when he has tried me, I shall come forth as gold* (NASB).

For if I am deficient in steadfastness and faith in such truths as *The prospect of the righteous is joy* (Proverbs 10:28a, NIV); *my heart trusts in Him, and I am helped* (Psalm 28:7b, ESV); and *The fruit of that righteousness will be peace; its effect will be quietness and confidence forever* (Isaiah 32:17,

NIV); , then my life will not bear the much fruit of John 15 because I'm not abiding in my Christ. Even the absence or insufficient amount of one Christ-like trait can over-shadow the presence of any or all Christ-like traits which might be present in the soil of my soul. (This principle is especially true with humility.) Proverbs 11:22 captures this idea, *Like a gold ring in a pig's snout is a beautiful woman without discretion* (ESV). Every Christ-like trait needs to be ready and available for use in any and every situation in the soil of my soul if my life is to reflect Him as He truly is - trustworthy, faithful, kind, loving, merciful, gracious, and worthy of all honor and glory (see Philippians 2:6-11).

I cannot mimic a true growth in faith despite my best efforts and my own plans and lies that "I am enough", "I got this", or "I can do it". These lies only produce weak, yellowed, stunted, and thin truth-deficient beliefs that don't survive when troubles come, much less when they come and stay over multiple seasons of my life. Worse yet, these lies produce seeds of doubt in God that just maybe He doesn't hear or answer prayer, much less stay close by no matter what (see Hebrews 13:5). Even my best attempts at adding distractions, possessions, busyness, or seemingly important responsibilities for seemingly important people, will not make up for the deficiency of joy and contentment which are hallmarks of a John 15 life.

Yet, if I am willing to let my life principles, and thus my daily life-choices, be tested, both by Scripture and by accountability to those who hold hard to what is true, then there is the far better chance of a harvest of Christ-likeness in my life and others. When I make the easy choice to say that all is fine as it is now, I deceive myself about my deficiency of humility and other necessary traits of a Christ-follower. Likewise, the testing of true faith in the life of a mature Christian (rich in fruit of the Spirit in Galatians 5:22-23) shows me that only His grace is sufficient for everything, especially and including my weakness (see 2 Corinthians 12:9). When I am accepting the truth in my weaknesses, then I am made complete in His strength resting on me (again 2 Corinthians 12:9). Then, my faith will grow as it should – rooted in truth, watered in love, and nourished by hope. And the soil of my soul will be distinctive in steadily holding fast to the truth of Scripture and the presence of Christ for today and days to come.

Digging Deeper

Take some time to look up, write out, and meditate on each of the Scriptures presented in this chapter.

1. 1 Thessalonians 5:21   2. Psalm 37:4

3. Proverbs 3:5-6   4. Ephesians 4:15   5. Proverbs 18:10

6. 1 John 1:9   7. James 1:2-4   8. Job 23:10

9. Proverbs 10:28   10. Isaiah 32:17   11. Proverbs 11:22
12. Philippians 2:6-11   13. Hebrews 13:5

14. Galatians 5:22-23   15. 2 Corinthians 12:9

What Scripture(s) made you stop and think about the status of the soil of your soul today? Why? (Note: you are not limited to those verses listed in this chapter, be especially conscious of those other verses brought to your mind and heart by the Holy Spirit).

What Scripture(s) do you need to return to tomorrow to receive more of the Holy Spirit's work on the soil of your soul and why?

Are you holding back any principles in your life from the truth of 1 Thessalonians 5:21? If so, take some time to think through and pray through what you hold as dear to your heart and life to see if they line up with Scripture and help you exhibit Christ-like characteristics in your life.

Name one Christ-like characteristic that others have commented on seeing in your life. Write out a prayer of thanksgiving to God for the presence of this gift in your life.

Name one Christ-like characteristic that you recognize as deficient in your life. Write out a prayer of supplication to God for the strength to trust Him in all ways for the growth of this characteristic in the soil of your soul starting today.

Which of the six essential components of good ground do you think you need the most today for your soul? Steadfastness, humility, obedience, vision, exaltation, and love. Why?

Take some time to pray for the continued good work of God to be done in the soil of your soul and life today. Write down at least three things you are thankful for today.

Reflection prayer:

Dear Father,

Thank You that You want truth in my inmost parts. Thank You that You gave me Your Word in Scripture that I can learn from You when I seek You in spirit and in truth. Thank You for the Holy Spirit Who prompts me to unearth every lie and expose it to You for removal and renewal. Please help me to not be afraid or lazy, but to diligently worship You in repentance and trusting obedience. Please help me to replace deficiencies in my faith with the abundance of abiding in Christ. Only You can do this – thank You that You will do this when I come to You!

In the strong Name of Jesus,

Amen.

7

Soil Texture and Falling into Place

Abide in Me and I in you. As the branch cannot bear fruit by itself, unless it abides in the vine, neither can you, unless you abide in me. I am the vine; you are the branches. Whoever abides in me and I in him, he it is that bears much fruit, for apart from me you can do nothing. If anyone does not abide in me he is thrown away like a branch and withers; and the branches are gathered, thrown into the fire, and burned. If you abide in me, and my words abide in you, ask whatever you wish, and it will be done for you.
John 15:4-7, ESV

Good Ground

Some of the most common analyses performed on soils include tests for determining soil pH, soil nutrient concentrations, and soil texture. Soil pH and nutrient concentration analyses usually are conducted annually or before each growing season to see if fertilizer or other amendments need to be added to maximize crop productivity and yield. However, soil texture analysis is usually only done infrequently as a soil's texture is an innate quality that rarely changes over time. Soil texture is so important a feature of a soil that it is a required part of an individual soil series name such as a Maury silt loam, a Piedmont clay loam, or any one of over 20,000 different individual soil series in the United States alone…

Knowing a soil's texture tells a soil scientist a whole lot about a soil's potential for crop productivity or other management outcomes; a soil's tendency towards flooding, erosion, or other drainage issues; and a soil's ability to provide nutrients and water to plants or support healthy macro or microorganism populations.

So, when this soil scientist was studying to teach a Sunday School lesson on the passage from John 15:4-7 of *Abide in Me and I in you*, she learned that a synonym for abide is "settle." And WOW! I nearly fell out of my chair because of the excitement from a whole new picture immediately settling into my head about the scientific process of soil texture analysis and the life-long process of abiding in Christ as seen in John 15. (Yes, I am that geeky eccentric soil science professor whose head nearly pops open with such

ideas! And who's so absent-minded that if I don't immediately write the ideas down, they're usually here and gone in
less time than they took to form!)

The picture that I began seeing as a Christian who's
a soil scientist, was how the technical scientific processes of
soil texture determination give me a better awareness of the
importance of choosing to abide, to settle, in Christ in all
aspects of my life so that much fruit can be borne from my
choices in life. And I hope that as we unpack this picture,
that you might be challenged in the same way too! Please
stay with me as I go into some of the details of the process
and terminology of soil texture analysis to show how it re-
lates to the fullness of abiding as seen in John 15. Trust me,
the picture at the end is definitely worth the work to get
there...

Soil texture is an innate characteristic of a soil determined by the relative amounts of sand, silt, and clay particles. Soil texture is considered by most soil scientists as the
primary indicator of a soil's fertility for both current and
future productivity. This is because soil texture is very influential in its impact on most soil characteristics.

There are twelve accepted soil textural classes based
upon a soil's relative amounts of sand, silt, and clay. As humans, we cannot change a soil's natural textural class large-
scale in the environment. We can only modify the textural
class of soil samples to be used in a laboratory or greenhouse.
God alone chooses a natural soil's textural class by how He
combines the sand, silt, and clay fractions in a soil horizon.

Soil textures can vary widely across a landscape, both horizontally and vertically.

Soil texture can be determined in the field by a soil scientist trained in assessing the amounts of sand, silt, and clay through how these three types of particles feel by touch. Just as muscle memory is essential to the performance of an athlete or musician, a trained sensitivity in touch from much prior experience with known samples of certain soil textures is essential for proper classification at the field level by a soil scientist. Quick and accurate qualitative analysis and classification of a soil's texture in the field can add a lot of insight to other decisions that a soil scientist needs to make at that time and place.

A soil scientist can't just decide how a silty clay, a clay loam, or a sandy loam feels based on how she thinks it should feel. A soil scientist must have had the proper extensive training with scientifically analyzed samples in the laboratory to be able to assign an unknown soil sample to its correct soil textural class in the field. With such training, a soil scientist's fingers and touch are properly calibrated to the twelve known classes to be able to identify an unknown soil sample to be placed in the category of a known texture. This training is key to provide continuity of data collection and comparison in a set of known and accepted standards for soil texture independent of personal bias, location, or time.

Even though soil scientists working as soil classifiers in the field have extensive training for determining soil texture by touch, a specific measurement of soil texture must also be done in the laboratory to provide supporting data for the analysis they've done in the field. Soil texture determination in the laboratory is a very precise and detailed process involving the measurement of the density of a soil sample suspension at set times during a set time period. Everything must be measured, timed, and calculated based on scientifically determined rates, times, and data.

For these analyses, density is considered to be the mass of the soil sample per the unit volume of the total suspension of soil sample, water, and added chemicals at specific time intervals. These measurements reflect the principle that the heaviest and largest particles (sands) fall first; followed by the medium particles of the silts; and the lightest and smallest clay particles fall last or remain in suspension. Then, the density measurements at the set times will reflect the amounts of sands, silts, and clays contained in the soil sample at that specific point in time. The measured quantities of sands, silts, and clays at those times will determine where the soil sample lands in the previously mentioned twelve accepted soil textural classes. Usually, the quantitative determination (laboratory numbers) of the soil sample's textural class matches the qualitative determination (field "feel") of the soil sample's textural class of an experienced and well-trained soil scientist, but not always.

To do a analysis of soil texture in the lab, an unknown soil sample is collected, dried, finely ground, precisely weighed, and then mixed with an also precisely measured amount of water and chemicals. This mix of soil, water, and chemicals is then placed into a large cylinder; vigorously shaken end-over-end (with a lid on the open end and a hand firmly fixed on both ends) and carefully placed onto a level surface for a certain measured time. During this time, density measurements are taken at specific times, for sand, silt, and clay over a 24-hour period. These measurements are then calibrated against known standards calculated for the measurements corresponding to certain soil textures. All of this data corresponds to set ranges of density measurement values for each specific type of soil texture such as a silty clay loam, sandy clay, or one of the remaining ten soil textural classes.

Hang in there, dear reader – we are almost there to the full picture! The cylinders used in soil texture analysis are called settling jars. The designated times for measurement of density for sand, silt, and clay particles are called settling times. Each type of soil particle has an appointed settling time because of its size and weight. This soil scientist hopes that your ears are perking up at the word "settling" – it's gonna get really good very soon!

A specific chemical mixture is also added to the soil and water suspension to help break the attraction between soil particles that makes them into aggregates. These bonds have to be physically broken (grinding and mixing) as well as chemically broken via the chemical mixture to get the necessary separation of the aggregates into individual soil particles. True measurements of soil texture are based upon the true amounts of each type of soil particle of sand, silt, and clay. Without vigorous mixing and chemical addition, true measurements could not be obtained because the natural soil aggregates have not been broken into individual soil particles. An example of this is that large or medium-sized clumps of clays can mimic sand or silt particles and thus give false readings of their amounts and ultimately, the wrong soil texture designation will be assigned to that soil sample. On the opposite side of this, individual clay particles can be so tiny they will never fall out of suspension because they weigh less than the water itself. This phenomenon is why many farm or water retention ponds often look muddy or cloudy because of the forever-suspended clay particles in the waters of ponds like these.

Keeping all of these details about soil texture determination and John 15:4-7 in mind, the picture that I saw was that for the true measure of my abiding, i.e., the settling of my life in Christ, I must allow every piece of my life, including my dreams and desires, to be taken apart into individual particles of trust, faith, and obedience. And for this separation to occur, I must fully submit to the removal of the natural attractions of self, pride, and personal agendas.

Self, pride, and personal agendas only deceive me by binding me up in the lies that they will give me the true measures of a devoted Christian life of joy, courage, and hope. Yet, all they give are false readings that happiness is found in what I can do and what I can get for myself. To think of this pervasive lie in soil science terms – I deceive myself in thinking that if I have a greater density of control on my life, this will produce a better measurement of life for me. It's all too easy to believe the lie that if I can have all the things in all the places and times, then I have a measure of control of my life. And if I have that measure of control, I have everything needed for an abundant life, all by myself. Unfortunately, these deceitful binding agents of pride, self, and personal agendas can be so strong that God uses times of crisis, turmoil, trial, and even upheaval in my life to remove their hold on me so that I can begin to listen and learn and thus, to settle and abide.

Challenging times can act as means of separating me into what God considers as a true measure for me as His child – obedience in every particle of my life. For when every particle of me is separated, I realize that I am not in control (nor ever really was). Only then are my heart and life ready to be used as good soil by God. For only then will I be obedient to *cease striving and know that* He is *God* (Psalm 46:10, NASB 1995) as I have truly settled into the place of abiding with God.

During those challenging times of vigorous shaking in my life, when my life's jar is seemingly turned end-over-end, the large sands of that which I can't easily control (future, health, others) usually fall quickly; the medium-sized silts of that which I think I have influence over (finances, job, relationships) fall next; and then the tiny clays of that which I believe I can control (schedule, others' perceptions of me, personal rights) usually linger on, resisting the pull to settle, to abide. Those seemingly small, insignificant clays of self are often the most influential in the true measure of my obedience. Yet my persistent God doesn't give up or turn away from me when those tiny stubborn self-clays refuse to settle. He doesn't let go when these stubborn clays try to give the false measurement that just because I don't feel His presence that He isn't there (see Hebrews 13:5). And when these persistent pervasive self-clays muddy my view of Christ, others cannot see the pure, clean, living water of Christ in my life (see Jeremiah 2:12-13 and John 7:38). Others can't know that only in seeking the abundant life of abiding in Christ for themselves will they find freedom and hope drawn from the well that will never run dry (see John 4:11).

One of the most precious thoughts from this picture about the intersection of abiding in Christ and soil texture determination is that no matter how vigorous the end-over-end shaking of the jar of my life, God always has a firm grip on me. I can know with confidence that my name has been engraved onto the very palms of His Hands (see Isaiah 49:16) and nothing can remove me from His Hands (see John 10:28). He will never turn away or leave (see Hebrews 13:5) as He alone is faithful and true (see Revelation 19:11). Like God, these truths don't change. They are not influenced by feelings, circumstances, or time.

My heart's response to the fall of each of these particles of my life is a direct measurement of what truly abides in my heart - love for Christ or self; humility or pride; grace or selfishness; and so on. And this response can reflect my heart's texture as good soil (or not) for the work of Christ, both now and in the future. For the texture of my heart directly impacts the characteristics of my life in obedience to Christ – Does his living water flow in and through me? How much attention and energy do I have to devote to battling pride rather than bearing fruit? What is my soul's vulnerability to being eroded by sin? And, so many more characteristics vital to my heart's soil being fertile ground (or not) for the work of God.

I desire a heart made of good soil – soft, fertile, deep, well-drained, and life-promoting – where humility, gratitude, obedience, and devotion thrive in their influence on every particle of my life. Truly the texture of the soil of my heart will greatly influence the fruit borne from my life and the likelihood of that yearned-for harvest of Matthew 13:23, *As for what was sown on good soil, this is the one who hears the word and understands it. He indeed bears fruit and yields, in one case a hundredfold, in another sixty, and in another thirty* (ESV).

Digging Deeper

Take some time to look up, write out, and meditate on each of the Scriptures presented in this chapter.

1. John 15:4-7   2. Hebrews 13:5   3. Jeremiah 2:12-13

4. John 7:38   5. John 4:11   6. Hebrews 13:5

7. Revelation 19:11   8. Matthew 13:23

What Scripture(s) made you stop and think about the status of the soil of your heart today? Why? (Note: you are not limited to those verses listed in this chapter, be especially conscious of those other verses brought to your mind and heart by the Holy Spirit).

What Scripture(s) do you need to return to tomorrow to receive more of the Holy Spirit's work on the soil of your heart and why?

Which of the six essential components of good ground do you think you need the most today for your soul? Humility, obedience, patience, trust, quietness, or perseverance. Why?

Are you in a challenging time in your life? Do you feel like your life is being turned end-over-end? If so, which of these Scriptures speaks truth to you that you need to hold fast to as you are in crisis? Which of these Scriptures do you need to share with a friend or family member in a challenging time in their life?

Take some time to pray for the continued good work of God to be done in the soil of your soul and life today. Write down at least three things you are thankful for today.

Good Ground

Reflection prayer:

Dear Father,

Thank You that You have always had a plan for good for my life. Thank You that in You there is true hope for now and the future. Thank You that nothing is beyond Your control. Please use these days as a way to draw me closer to You and to soften the soil of my soul for Your will. Please remove pride and selfishness from my life and replace it with humility and grace.

In the strong Name of Jesus,

Amen.

8

NEW GROUND

So neither the one who plants nor the one who waters is any-thing, but only God, who makes things grow. The one who plants and the one who waters have one purpose, and they will each be rewarded according to their own labor. For we are co-workers in God's service; you are God's field, God's building.
1 Corinthians 3:7-9, NIV

When one of my soil science professors in college start-ed the class by saying "Ok folks, listen closely, we've got lots of ground to cover today", I knew that was not just a figure of speech, much less an expression to be taken lightly. Rather, that phrase meant that I was in for a lot of hard work of concentrating and trying to tie many thoughts together, probably while simultaneously trying to do an experiment or solving a set of problems. Days like that were pretty common in most of my soil science classes because the study of soil science includes biology, chemistry, physics, hydrology, geology, climatology, engineering, entomology, plant science, and microbiology. So, if my students hear a similar speech from me at the beginning of class, they know we do indeed have lots of ground to cover. And if we're on a field trip, those are words to be taken both literally and figuratively which translates to "walk fast and listen faster!"

In a soil science class, there is usually lots of ground to cover and much of that is new ground, especially in the breadth of an introductory soil science course that tries to hit the high spots of the many different topics of soil science. It is JOY for me to walk with students on new ground – to explore a wealth of new ideas and connections which can be fertile ground for a new appreciation of the beauty inherent in creation and its Creator. I love the opportunity to open Bibles and textbooks together with notebooks and pens in the middle of our desks, lab benches, or laps in the classroom, lab room, or field. For there we discover together the richness of natural and Biblical truths working in a most magnificent mutualism (biology term for where the whole is greater than the sum of the parts) with each other. As delightful as discovery and learning are for me (and hopefully, my students too), it does take a lot of hard focused work to cut a furrow into the rich gift of new ground.

Similarly, in farming, new ground, or ground that has not been plowed or planted before (or at least not for very many years), has long been considered to be the most desirable. New ground usually has higher organic matter contents, better soil structure development, established micro and macro-organism populations, and other traits leading to a greater soil fertility resulting in better crop growth and production. This idea is seen in the phrase describing the process of trying something different or not before encountered - "breaking up new ground". This phrase captures the hard work of using a new way of thinking with different ideas and connections and finding them to be ripe ground for beautiful solutions to previously knotty or unsolved problems.

The pioneers experienced the bounty of new ground when they used the moldboard plow to cut a swath across the Midwestern United States. The moldboard plow, "the plow that broke the prairie's back" with its steel shank, was the only implement strong enough to break apart the incredibly dense root systems of those thick prairie grasses. Yet the pioneers learned after a few years of plowing those prairie soils that the fertility of the new ground could decline if the soils weren't properly managed. This decline in fertility season by season would often then prompt the pioneers to take up stakes and move further west seeking more and more new ground.

In a similar vein, the lifestyle of subsistence farming has occurred for years in Central and South America. Subsistence farming consists of a farmer and his family moving into an untouched portion of the rainforest; cutting down the trees; burning back the remaining above-ground material; and then planting a crop on the new ground. Upon the first plowing of rainforest soils, all looks very promising with dark, lush topsoil that just had a fresh shot of nitrogen from the burned plant residue which was incorporated into the soil during plowing. And yes, this new ground is very fertile for about three to five years until the organic matter degrades and the thin topsoil layer erodes down to the concrete-like subsoil of these very fragile soil ecosystems. Then it's time to move and start the process all over again on new ground...

The subsistence farming system has worked for thousands of years with the small family plots but with the advent of large-scale corporation farming, rainforests are quickly being stripped and forever lost due to poor choices and the ravages of time on fragile ecosystems. Even if the area is left alone to return to native vegetation, the climax community of the rainforest cannot be achieved because of the myriad of interrelationships dependent on the soil and its inhabitants that are now gone. These interrelationships require inputs and diverse populations of everything from microbes to mammals in specific placement and numbers for their establishment, much less their maintenance. Such fragile ecosystems on such fragile soil systems are not resilient enough to overcome misguided attempts at conventional agricultural productivity.

Many soil scientists (including me) marvel at how such poor soils can support such a vibrant and ecologically diverse rainforest ecosystem on about six inches of top-soil overlying glorified concrete. As a Christian who's a soil scientist, I think these rainforest systems are held together by God, along with the rest of creation, in ways no one may ever fully understand (see Isaiah 55:8-9). All parts of these ecosystems are major players in the health and longevity of such systems, and thus, all parts are essential to the productivity– be they biotic (living participants in the ecosystem like plants, microorganisms, and animals) or abiotic (non-living participants like air, water, and weather). To me, these systems represent God's patient, continual, and faithful application of a strong and resilient grace to his creation. He never will turn away from such care for creation and us, His created (see Hebrews 13:5).

Today new ground is not plentiful as in days past, but it still can be found. New ground is now usually found in small fields once under production on small family farms converted into timber production or completely abandoned by children who didn't return to the farm as adults. Whatever the reason for the disuse of the ground in the past, the turnover and planting of new ground can indicate new hope for the future.

Yet as good as new ground is in fertility for growing wheat, corn, or cotton, it is not good ground if you want to grow legumes like soybeans, peanuts, or lentils. This is because all of these crops (and others) are in the bean family, *Fabaceae*, which have a most interesting and beautiful association with the soil bacteria, *Rhizobia.* New ground usually doesn't have a population of native Rhizobia bacteria, and legumes usually don't flourish without the Rhizobia living on their roots. The legume plants provide the water, growing surface, sugars, and other nutrients to the bacteria while the bacteria provide nitrogen to the bean plant in a form it can use. These amazing *Rhizobia* bacteria take nitrogen from the air and transform this nitrogen into forms the plant can utilize right there at the roots where the plants would normally take it up from the ground. This process is called nitrogen fixation. These *Rhizobia* bacteria form nodules or little round, callous skin growths on the roots that if sliced open, are red on the inside from the oxygenated hemes of the bacteria similar to our own red blood cells (hemoglobin) – isn't that just so neat!

Fungi are the important third party in this plant-microbe association for successful bean production. The fungi have lots of little hyphae (like unimaginably long, skinny fingers) that grow around, between, and through soil making very important linkages between the soil, bacteria, plants, and fungi. These hyphae provide an astronomical amount of surface area for faster, more efficient nutrient and water uptake from the soil for the microorganisms and plants. The hyphae also provide a measure of protection against some soil-borne plant diseases.

The fungi are not as "picky" about soil environments as the *Rhizobia* bacteria, so there's a good chance that they are present even in new ground. But even if the new ground has fungi in place, it most likely won't have a native population of the *Rhizobia* bacteria. Therefore, if you try and grow legumes on new ground without adding healthy *Rhizobia* bacteria, you will most likely end up with sad-looking sickly stunted beans that don't have nodules and thus, insufficient nitrogen for the needs of the crop. I think of this addition (inoculation) of Rhizobia to the soil to be like having to use starter with mature yeast populations for sourdough or Amish friendship bread so that your bread will rise and be tasty.

New ground can be inoculated with *Rhizobia* bacteria by mixing in residue or composts from a legume crop grown elsewhere; buying legume seed sprayed with dried bacteria; or applying a liquid containing these bacteria across the field. Usually, the second and third choices give the least desirable results because the bacteria that are being applied are not native to the soil or could be the wrong type ("strain") of bacteria. For example, soybean specific strains of *Rhizobia* won't thrive in association with alfalfa, peanuts, clover, or any other bean crop, regardless of all these crops being in the same *Fabaceae* family as soybeans. To borrow a phrase from my students, the different strains of *Rhizobia* "just don't play well with others".

No one fully understands all the interrelationships involved for a successful soybean harvest, much less those factors yet unknown in this system. Yet this principle is well-known: if any of the necessary components to this system of soil, plant, bacteria, and fungi are not present, the system fails. Furthermore, if these components are not in the right measure or proportion for each and every one of the system participants, the system also fails. The soil must have the right pH, moisture, and fertility levels while the bacteria must have sufficient population numbers for inoculation of the plant roots and subsequent growth during the growing season. The fungi must also have sufficient population numbers and amounts of hyphae spread across the field. The bean seeds must be good and viable ones with proper spacing as to guarantee lack of competition with neighboring plants during the growing season. And that doesn't even include the weather or climate conditions necessary for germination, growth, flowering, and bean production. As importantly, these soil, microbial, plant, and climate/weather conditions required for growth and productivity must be present at the beginning and all the way through the growing season up to harvest to make for a healthy crop. Good farmers know the required conditions and work diligently to do what they can to maintain such conditions at all times. Yet they fully know that there are conditions, such as weather and soil type, beyond their control and always at work, either for or against them.

These specific interrelationships between the soil, bean plants, bacteria, and fungi remind me of 1 Corinthians 3:7-9 which says, *So neither the one who plants nor the one who waters is anything, but only God, who makes things grow. The one who plants and the one who waters have one purpose, and they will each be rewarded according to their own labor. For we are co-workers in God's service; you are God's field, God's building* (NIV).

The real force behind any kind of work, be it farming for soybeans or for souls, is *only God, who makes things grow.* Nothing can replace the presence of God in and at work in an activity, organization, or plan as to what is ultimately produced in, from, and through the venture. God alone is the force that overshadows the germination, growth, and harvest of the fields of our lives. He alone is the One who can bring forth the abundance of fruit necessary to feed both the bellies and the souls of our world. He alone can make and remake the soil of our souls to be fertile new ground for His righteousness and kingdom yet to come (see Matthew 6:33).

No matter how hard I may work at, invest in, or dream of something, if God is not present and active and at the center of it all the way through the entire time required for the work, that something will not grow, much less thrive, into producing that *100-fold harvest* of Mark 4:20. Just as I can't hold my hands out and stop a thunderstorm, I can't barter for, manufacture, or purchase the unmistakable working of God to restore broken marriages and prodigal children; break addictions and co-dependencies; trade bitterness for forgiveness; exchange regret, guilt, and shame for freedom; or overcome rejection, defeat, and arrogance to unite hearts in a singular mission for His Name to be made known to the nations (see Matthew 28:18-20).

Only He is greater than even sin's devastation that can sweep across our lives, divide us, and try to leave us with hearts and lives bare of hope, courage, and joy. Only He can bring life from that which before was dead. He alone can make new soil in a soul where there is nothing but the dirt of sin. He alone can bring life where there is none. This soil scientist knows that full well. And when He does do such incredible things as these, His work is as distinctive and as energizing as His power described in 2 Corinthians 4:7, *But we have these treasure in jars of clay, to show that the surpassing power belongs to God and not to us* (ESV). His work is distinctive because He was the one who did it, not me.

Just as *Rhizobia* bacteria cannot be substituted with something else, the presence of God in a work cannot be substituted or duplicated. Like the absence of *Rhizobia* is clearly seen throughout the growing season in sickly, stunted, yellowing, thin, weak, plants with shriveled or empty bean pods, the absence of God in a work is seen in the attitudes of those involved as self-focused, driven, unaware, or apathetic. The absence of the freshness, the power of God's presence is missing from the work, and nothing can substitute for it.

When my focus is myself, all I can see is the numbers in attendance, likes on social media, spoken or written "atta-girls", or monies in the accounts. And then I am believing the lie that this data indicates the favor of God is upon "my ministry" because "numbers don't lie." With the cloud of my arrogance ever looming over my life, for me, even the use of the phrase, "my ministry", could indicate a lack of His work in the doing and my belief of the lie of "me, me, me". This lie compares with the soybean harvest which was dependent on added nitrogen fertilizer because the field wasn't properly inoculated with the *Rhizobia* bacteria – yes, there was a harvest, but it focused on "my ministry", I am either deceived in the "me is enough" mentality or I am ignorant of the more, that abundantly exceedingly more, present only when God is in the work as with Ephesians 3:20-21.

Please know that my fingers are trembling as I dare to write these thoughts. Like Paul, I am *the chief of sinners* (1 Timothy 1:15, KJ21). I am that arrogant one who constantly struggles with the cheap satisfaction found in "look at me and what I can do," which is only magnified by the scientist in me who wants to live by the data and the little girl in me who longs for acceptance and approval by others. Yet I have experienced the unmistakable unforgettable difference of when God is the One doing, bringing, changing, and growing the lives of all involved in the work. This difference, His difference, can quickly be seen in the work, be it with two or two thousand people all *gathered in His Name*, not in mine (Matthew 18:20, ESV).

And as distinctively, the fruit of His work is incomparably sweet and satisfying! That true Vine-ripened fruit of John 15 and Galatians 5 makes me yearn for even more and more of this kind of fruit. This yearning, in turn, draws me closer in to Jesus, in the hope found in prayer while holding hard to His faithful promises, to such truths like the one expressed in James 5:16b with *the prayer of a godly person is powerful. Things happen because of it* (NIRV).

Many times, when God is at work, the harvest may not come when I think it should or in the manner that I think it should, and I'm discouraged in it. Worse yet, I'm disappointed in such a harvest where I'm not recognized as I think I should be for all of "my" hard work. Such an attitude of "it's all about me" mentality ignores the true need for me to be praying for God to be present, to be glorified, and to be calling up and out those dedicated workers needed for the *fields ripe for harvest* (John 4:35, NIV).

God-appointed and God-equipped workers are people who love their Jesus deeply, and thus, the people to whom they have been sent. They love with the glorious good news of the Gospel, both in word and in deed. This unmistakable unforgettable kind of love makes for the distinctive work of a disciple which is often misunderstood, overlooked, or considered unimportant to those who don't embrace the economy of God where the little is made much as in Luke 16:10. After all, washing feet isn't the most respected or sought after of professions and doesn't produce those desired attendance numbers, likes, "atta-girls", or dollar bills.

Only a constant seeking of God's presence via humility in prayer and the plowing of new ground of the soil of my soul for a deeper obedience can bring the hidden, fertile power of the little to the surface of my life. And there at the surface where it can't be ignored, the humility of the little softens the soil of my soul, thus preparing it for God's work. Humility's hyphae strengthens the necessary interrelationships of joy, courage, peace, faith, and hope in a way that can't be duplicated or replaced. And in turn, these interrelationships of a living dynamic trust in my Christ promotes the growth of prayer which in turn, draws me into His presence and I am changed there – cultivated, if you will, for His purpose of planting and harvest. This is the cycle of true life that leads to more and more new ground open for planting in the soil of my soul. For only God can take the very little of me presenting myself *as a living sacrifice, holy and acceptable to God, which is your spiritual act of worship* (Romans 12:1, NCB) and use this as a means of working in mine and others' lives for a harvest of His glory for kingdom come, for the now and for eternity. Now that's the kind of harvest this soil scientist wants to be a little part of starting today and onwards in tomorrow!

Digging Deeper

Take some time to look up, write out or read (as specified), and meditate on each of the Scriptures presented in this chapter.

1. 1 Corinthians 3:7-9   2. Isaiah 55:8-9

3. Hebrews 13:5   4. Matthew 6:33   5. Mark 4:20

6. Matthew 28:18-20   7. 2 Corinthians 4:7

8. Ephesians 3:20-21   9. 1 Timothy 1:15

10. Matthew 18:20   11. John 15:1-8

12. Galatians 5:22-23   13. James 5:16   14. John 4:35

15. Luke 16:10   16. Romans 12:1-2

Good Ground

What Scripture(s) made you stop and think about the status of the soil of your soul today? Why? (Note: you are not limited to those verses listed in this chapter, be especially conscious of those other verses brought to your mind and heart by the Holy Spirit).

What Scripture(s) do you need to return to tomorrow to receive more of the Holy Spirit's work on the soil of your soul and why?

Name at least 3 of the best things you've received from having a relationship with Jesus. Take some time to outline these things in a simple form that you could use to tell someone in your home, neighborhood, workplace, or church small group about how Jesus has changed your life using these 3 things.

Have you ever seen or been a part of a ministry that was full (to the brim) with the power of Jesus alive and at work in it? If so, what characteristics made this ministry distinctively different from other types of ministries you've seen?

What changes do you yearn for Christ to make in your life starting today? Why did you choose these particular changes over others?

Which of the six essential components of good ground do you think you need the most today for your soul? Steadfastness, humility, obedience, vision, exaltation, and love. Why?

Take some time to pray for the continued good work of God to be done in the soil of your soul and life today. Write down at least three things you are thankful for today.

Reflection prayer:

> *Dear Father,*
>
> *Thank You that You alone are mighty and can do the work You deem best. Thank You that You allow me to be a part of Your work here on earth. Thank You that You change me as I trust You in the work and how You choose to do it. Please help me to trust You more today even if I don't see results of You at work in the lives of those around me. Please help me to pray with increasing fervency and urgency for Your kingdom to come as the days grow closer to the return of Your Son, Jesus Christ.*
>
> *In the strong Name of Jesus,*
>
> *Amen.*

9

BEYOND WHAT I CAN UNDERSTAND

I will give you the treasures of darkness and the hoards in secret places, that you may know it is I, the Lord, the God of Israel, who call you by your name.
Isaiah 45:3, ESV

While reading a wonderful book this morning, *The Fragrance of God*, this quote was immediately etched on my mind and heart – "Where spirit and earth mix, God and man meet".[2] I identify with this thought as some of my most memorable worship experiences have occurred in the woods with head bowed and hands lifted with soil falling through my fingers. I meet with God as He meets with me. And the very thought of that is overwhelming – the God of all creation stoops to lift my head and listen to me, His created. There is a special beauty when the soil of my soul lies exposed before Him, ready for cultivation and change into the Image of His Son, the Christ. The Unchanging Christ Who was there at creation, is here with me now, and will remain forever (see Colossians 1:15-17 and Revelation 1:8).

The action of sifting soil through my fingers reminds me of the beauty of returning ash to ash and dust to dust. When I do this, I am reminded of the necessity of my death so that His life may flourish in me. It's as if when my hands are full of soil, the soil of my soul is open to God and ready for His work to be done in it. And as the soil falls through my fingers to return to the soil under my feet, the soil of my soul joins it in a surrender to worship. Confession, repentance, and surrender should be my natural responses there in worship. And these will then lead to the death of my will. For I know that the choice of my obedience is precious in His sight (see 1 Samuel 15:22 and 2 Corinthians 7:15).

When I was doing research for my Ph.D., I spent many hours mixing soil with my hands in prepping samples for experiments. I quickly grew tired of running all the equipment, collecting all the data, and especially doing all the calculations, but never of working with the soil itself. Even though my hands would ache from hours of soil preparation, it was as if the aches themselves were physical reminders of the presence and closeness of Creator God. And now, years later, the same feelings remain. The longer I work with my hands in soil, the deeper I think and the more I discover – be it about whatever I am evaluating in the soil or the condition of the soil of my soul before the penetrating gaze of God.

My Ph.D. research focused on a specific group of soil microorganisms – the denitrifiers. Denitrifiers are a group of bacteria usually found deep in subsoil near the ground-water table. Denitrifiers can grow with or without oxygen being present in the soil environment. This adaptability makes the denitrifiers well-qualified to thrive in the deep subsoil environment which is periodically flooded and thus, often lacking oxygen. They can thrive in such environments because their systems can easily switch from using oxygen to using other elements in place of oxygen without loss of growth or health.

These bacteria are called denitrifiers because they convert nitrogen present in the soil from forms the plants can use into a form most plants can't use for growth. They are quite literally "de-nitrifying" or removing available nitrogen in the soil from the plants and other microorganisms.

For years, denitrifying bacteria were considered undesirable because of their removal of plant-available nitrogen from soil. Thus, much research was done to try and slow, if not altogether stop, their activity. There was emphasis on this type of research because the loss of plant usable nitrogen from the soil during the denitrification process often represented a major loss of money spent on nitrogen fertilizer not used by the crop and subsequent loss of crop productivity in yield at harvest.

However, not long before I began my Ph.D. research, some soil scientists proposed that the denitrifiers might be a potential way to clean up a big environmental problem at that time. The problem was soil contamination from buried underground storage tanks leaking gasoline or other fuels at airports, gas stations, and large commercial farms. These tanks were often buried at depths of about twenty-five feet deep in the soil. The problem with this depth in the soil is that this was often at the intersection of the groundwater table zone where water levels and thus, oxygen levels, in the soil fluctuated periodically. Therefore, denitrifier bacteria were possible solutions for remediating this situation since they could survive in these environments. Another issue with this depth in the soil is that the metal fuel storage tanks were susceptible to rusting and subsequently, leaking, because of the fluctuating water levels. Worse yet, the fluctuating groundwater levels and rusting storage tanks made for the perfect storm of subsequent offsite water pollution from the leaked fuels into other vulnerable regions containing wells, aquifers, lakes, etc., since water flows both horizontally and vertically in soils.

At that time in the 1990s, conventional remediation methods for the contaminated soils at leaky, buried fuel tank sites involved digging up the entire area; carrying off the contaminated soil; and either burning this soil or putting it in a landfill. The solution was almost as bad as the problem itself. Thus, the idea that denitrifiers might be able to degrade the fuel that had leaked into the soil and groundwater was very attractive for multiple reasons – the contaminated soil could be left in place for remediation after the leaky tank was removed; native soil bacteria wouldn't be a potential risk for other issues during/after their degradation of the fuel leaked from the tank; and cost of cleanup by the denitrifiers was much less than conventional methods.

Thankfully, it's now illegal to bury fuel storage tanks in the ground without proper containment measures such as being encapsulated by concrete so we aren't facing new contaminated sites like these. We know enough now not to repeat our mistakes of the past and how to try and remediate such mistakes as these fuel-contaminated sites and bodies of water.

Yet even now, many years later, no one fully understands the interactions of all the participants in the system for remediating fuel-contaminated soil ecosystems. We can apply the treatments that work and can get desirable results even without understanding the how's or why's of the solution variables. All of the participants: denitrifiers, soil, groundwater, fuel chemicals, tanks, nearby bodies of water, topography, climate, and people, were (and are) inextricably linked in a mind-bogglingly complex ecosystem that we could only try and wrap our minds around.

Good Ground

My research was, at best, a stab in the dark of trying to get a handle on what was happening and a few potential ways we might influence system outputs. I can remember thinking "these denitrifiers are simply magnificent in how they can live, much less thrive, in this environment! I can't understand this and that's okay! This is nothing I've done but I'm allowed to see this happen, again and again! Thank you, Lord, for this!"

God gave me the gift of being able to show that de-nitrifying bacteria did indeed degrade fuel leaked into those contaminated subsoils. Even though I worked with these bacteria for four years, I never stopped being amazed that they could do such an incredible task as "eating" these fuels by converting them into harmless gases that then escaped into the atmosphere. And now, over twenty years later, I am still in awe of the fact that these microscopic bacteria could and can "eat" up the leaked fuels and transform these contaminants into gases that move into the atmosphere, thereby returning the soil to its pre-contaminated state. I couldn't even begin to understand how these bacteria did such a thing, much less how they thrived in the doing. Four years of intense study with hundreds of experiments yielding thousands of data points on that one process with the denitrifying bacteria only began to scratch the surface of its intricacy and beauty. And that's just one of hundreds or thousands of soil processes and cycles simultaneously occurring in the amazing world under our feet. Even now with all of our technology and advancements in monitoring and measurement, no one fully understands most of these soil processes, including soil scientists far more learned than me.

Yet God has been gracious to teach this arrogant soil scientist that an even more beautiful gift than being able to understand something fully is to know just enough of it to be able to wonder at the much more of it. For in the lack of understanding, there is freedom knowing that God is in control of all processes, cycles, and organisms and has been since He spoke them into being at creation (see Genesis 1 and 2). Even if I were to have a lifetime of lifetimes to study a single soil process, I will never fully grasp it as I am not the One who created the process, set it into motion at creation, and has controlled it since (see Isaiah 55:8-9). And there is such freedom in the knowledge that I am not expected to understand, much less control it. My task is to trust the One who does understand and control all things. And thanks be to God, He provides all that is needed for me to trust Him, when I make the choice to do so.

It truly is my opportunity as a Christian who is a soil scientist, to glimpse the wonder in soil processes and to bow my head on the soil in worship to God. Yet the wonder doesn't stop there – it continues on in such thoughts as Isaiah 45:3, *I will give you the treasures of darkness and the hoards in secret places, that you may know it is I, the Lord, the God of Israel, who call you by your name* (ESV). This description of the treasures and wealth in the dark and secret places reminds me of denitrification and other soil processes, which God put into place for us to discover and find to be great helps for so many lives. His grace to us extends far beyond soil processes, science, and salvation. He has given us the wonder of the far more of redemption and righteousness through Christ whom even the most learned cannot fully understand.

I love the picture in Colossians 2:2b-3 which says *to reach all the riches of full assurance of understanding and the knowledge of God's mystery, which is Christ, in whom are hidden all the treasures of wisdom and knowledge* (ESV). My mind can never begin to comprehend these *treasures of wisdom and knowledge* hidden in my Christ. Yet He gives me repeated opportunities to discover more of His beauty in creation and His presence in prayer and Scripture, even when I don't delight in the doing, much less in the finding of Him already there waiting for me to come.

Many days even Christ can seem hidden amidst the noise of others' needs, pain, the unimportant, and my own pride. Yet I know that if I keep seeking Him and keep digging for those hidden treasures of wisdom and knowledge through prayer and obedient faith, He will give glimpses of the much more that lies beyond what I can see now, much less understand. He tells me that *the prospect of the righteous is joy* (Proverbs 10:28, ESV) so I keep digging in the hard ground of learning truth to find the buried treasure of joy to be my strength as promised in Nehemiah 8:10. And thus, my natural response is to express this joy with head bowed and hands full of soil lifted in worship to my Christ, *the im-*

age of the invisible God, the firstborn of all creation (Colossians 1:15, ESV) while the soil of my soul cries out "Hallelujah!"

Digging Deeper

Take some time to look up, write out or read (as specified), and meditate on each of the Scriptures presented in this chapter.

1. Isaiah 45:3   2. Colossians 1:15-17

3. Revelation 1:8   4. 1 Samuel 15:22

5. 2 Corinthians 7:15   6. Read Genesis chapters 1 and 2

7. Isaiah 55:8-9   8. Colossians 2:2-3

9. Proverbs 10:28   10. Nehemiah 8:10

What Scripture(s) made you stop and think about the status of the soil of your soul today? Why? (Note: you are not limited to those verses listed in this chapter, be especially conscious of those other verses brought to your mind and heart by the Holy Spirit).

Good Ground

What Scripture(s) do you need to return to tomorrow to receive more of the Holy Spirit's work on the soil of your heart and why?

Have you experienced situations or times in life where you don't understand what God is doing? If so, how did such times make you feel about trusting God in these times? And if so, what did you learn (or are learning) about God, others, and yourself from these times?

List at least 2-3 Scripture verses or passages which you don't fully understand. Do these verses/passages frustrate you or exhilarate you as you ponder them? Explain why you chose this answer.

Is there an area in your life now in which you feel out of control? If so, take some time to pray and ask God for wisdom and understanding for this situation and for yourself and others in this situation. If a Bible verse or passage comes to mind during this time of prayer, please make sure and take the time to look it up, read it carefully, and write it here with the date to mark this time as being in God's Hands and not your own.

Which of the six essential components of good ground do you think you need the most today for your soul? Steadfastness, humility, obedience, vision, exaltation, and love. Why?

Take some time to pray for the continued good work of God to be done in the soil of your soul and life today. Write down at least three things you are thankful for today.

Reflection prayer:

Dear Father,

Thank You that You alone understand everything, including that which seems frustrating or frightening to me now. Thank You that You give wisdom and understanding when I seek You for it. Thank You that You are in control of everything at all times with Your sovereign power, might, and Presence. Please help me not to be afraid but to trust You in all things, especially the unknown. Please give me the wisdom and the strength to follow Your leading even when the road seems dark. Please show me those treasures in darkness that You can use to bring light, joy, and hope to me and others through me.

In the strong Name of Jesus,
Amen.

Epilogue

More Discovery Lies Ahead

Open my eyes that I may see wonderful things in your law.
I am a stranger on earth; do not hide your commands from me.
My soul is consumed with longing for your laws at all times.
Psalm 119:18–20, NIV

❧

O ne of the most ingrained principles by which a scientist shapes her days and plans for the future is that
answering any good question by research will produce at
least three more good questions. Hence, science marches
on – not in defeat or feeling overwhelmed by now seeing
even more questions – but in the brightness of discovering

more and moving forward in hope towards that next bit of light. A scientist's job is never done but is always renewing and fulfilling, if she is seeking Creator God as the Source of truth, life, and light.

Similarly, a Christian should be shaping her days and plans for the future by finding more light from Scripture via the Holy Spirit showing truth, life, and faith. As she sees more of Christ in the Word, she will be encouraged to keep marching on in obedience, thus discovering more courage and joy while moving forward in hope towards bringing a new bit of light to those in her world. Her job is never done but she is always being renewed and fulfilled if she is seeking Creator God as her Source of truth, life, and light.

Hopefully, the Scripture and science we've unearthed in this book have brought more light to you and those in your world. There is always much more to discover, in science and especially in Scripture. And in the discovering, there is opportunity for developing more and more good ground in the soil of our souls. Christ yearns for more for us with Him as the Creator, Sustainer, and Caretaker of the creation around us and within us. His work will not be completed until His return.

With that thought in mind, I surely hope you'll join me in *Good Ground: Volume 2* coming soon from Northeastern Baptist Press. In *Volume 2*, we will dig deeper and cultivate more good ground in the soil of our souls for more of that *100-fold harvest* of Matthew 13:23. (Spoiler alert on *Good Ground: Volume 2*: we start where you were probably looking for in this book – with the parable of the soil, seed, and sower also found in Matthew 13. This soil scientist is so excited and grateful for you!)

Afterword

So I say to you, ask and keep on asking, and it will be given to you; seek and keep on seeking, and you will find; knock and keep on knocking, and the door will be opened to you.
Luke 11:9, AMP

⟡

Thank you, dear reader, for taking this journey with me. I am so grateful for YOU! Thank you for your patience, understanding, and grace towards me in this weak attempt to share a little bit of the glorious beauty found in my incredible Jesus and His creation. I have been praying for you while writing and editing this book. May the soil of your soul keep growing deeper, softer, and richer as you seek the treasures of hope, faith, and love found in the goodness of our Creator God. If you don't have a personal relationship with our Good God, please contact me at soul-scientistblog.com - I would LOVE to talk with you about the most wonderful Friend you can ever know. Introducing Him to you would be the very best day ever for me!

ENDNOTES

1 E. Vaughn, *Becoming Elizabeth Elliot* (Nashville: B&H Publishing, 2020), 15.

2 V. Guroian, *The Fragrance of God* (Grand Rapids: William B. Eerdmans Publishing Company, 2006), 43.

Dr. Madison and her granddaughter

About the Author

Dr. Beth Madison received a B.S. in Plant and Soil Science from the University of Tennessee, a M.S. in Soil Conservation from the University of Kentucky, and a Ph.D. in Soil Microbiology from Kansas State University. She currently teaches at Union University, and has previously taught at South Georgia State College, Western Kentucky University, Kansas State University and University of Kentucky. She has nearly twenty-five years of experience in teaching soil, plant, and environmental sciences, and nearly twenty years of teaching Bible studies to various audiences ranging from youth to senior adults.